The Horse Gods

Old Mama's Story

A Totally Fictitious Horse Tale

by Milly Hunt Porter

*I fondly dedicate this book to my children, who have taught
me so much, to all my grandchildren, from whom I have been
privileged to learn, and to my husband, who shares my life so
completely and who walks with me in the evenings.*

Published by
Give-It-A-Go Books
P.O. Box 248
Bruneau, Idaho 83604
208-845-2117

ISBN 0-9711386-0-5

The cover image is from an original watercolor
by Molly Pearce of Raymond, California

Foreword

The Horse Gods is an endearing tale that takes the reader on a thirty-plus-year journey. It touches on many of the theories that influenced the horse industry from the mid-1950s to the mid-1980s. For the most part, though, it is a people story—with all the ups and downs of life having been shared with the beloved family horse. This sensitive and tender-hearted horse narrates the story, thinking back in time and reliving her memories.

The story opens on a sunny day in early autumn, and the reader meets an aged mare, standing in the run of her long-time home in the San Joaquin Valley of California. At this period of her life, the mare is called Old Mama. However, as a young foal, her "people family" in northern Nevada called her Bonita, because she was so pretty. With the coming of her first foal, her second "people family" referred to her as Mama, only to change her name to Old Mama when she became in foal late in her life.

Much of what Old Mama remembers are the events and circumstances in the lives of the ones she considers "her people." Even though she wasn't always present when some of the events she narrates took place, during the day's work or at chore time, Old Mama would learn of them when the various members of "her people" shared these events—and their lives—with her.

—Elaine H. Black
April, 2001

Acknowledgments

I have been fortunate for over seventy years to have been covered by much corral dust. I have had the opportunity to observe years of growth and change in the horse world and to observe some of the best at their best. I owe a debt to all of those wonderful horses and capable horsemen and horsewomen.

For the opportunity to record and to share all the dust, I owe a debt of gratitude to many people. First, a special "thank you" goes to my daughter Elaine Black for her hours of effort on the computer. She was a model of patience with this project. I want to thank Jenny, Mary, Cheryl, Blenda, Marvin and Mary Ellen, George E., Gene and Helen, Ty and Ronda, Allie, Kaye, Molly, and Vicki for their insightful reader responses. I'm also grateful for Linda Prentiss who re-entered my life at just the right time to help with the transition from rough manuscript to final form and for all the enthusiasm she brought to the project.

1

The warm California sun filtered down through the grid above Old Mama's run. Old Mama liked it that way. It was the time of year between the long hot days and the days of little sunshine. Old Mama closed her eyes and tried to ignore the flies. She shifted her body so three legs supported her.

Lately she had noticed pain in her right hindquarters. It seemed to move from one joint to another. She had discovered three ways to live with it. She could just rest it, go a little easier, or just ignore it. Once she had heard an old cowboy say, "I'd rather wear out than rust out." To her that seemed the best way to go.

Today was a quiet day around the stables. There was an air of expectation and waiting. Boy and Golden Son were away, entered in a special contest held once a year. Many horses and riders were there. Only three-year-old horses were eligible for the sizable money purse, which was quite an honor to win.

Missy had gone up for the eliminations. Because Boy and Golden Son had been able to compete just the way they always worked at the stables, they had made it into the finals. It was a joy to watch them work together. Doing a reining pattern, working the mechanical cow or with a pen of lively yearlings, they were a team. Missy often saddled Old Mama and they would just walk out, to be where they could enjoy watching. Wise One had influenced so much of Boy's attitude toward Golden Son. Through the years, Wise One had made many visits to the stables.

As Old Mama half dozed, her mind drifted back through the years to when she was a foal at her mama's side. She was back in Nevada with the wild band, playing with the other foals. Golden Stallion watched carefully while they played "King of the Mountain!" and "Race Around the Sage Brush!" Being on the small side, younger than most of the rest, she wasn't the fastest, but no foal enjoyed the play more.

As the end of the long hot season neared, the band had to travel further to water. The streams that had been so full earlier had all dried up and little puffs of dust rose from each step, as the herd traveled. The afternoons often brought dust devils dancing through the dry heat.

One of the band's favorite watering holes was a small spring up a box canyon. Golden Stallion and Granny Mare always brought them in quite cautiously. The water from the spring was clear and cold, but Granny Mare knew they could pay a tremendous price for it. With a series of large boulders hanging over the spring, it could be a place for a mountain lion to leap upon a foal; in the year before that very thing had happened to one of the older mare's foals.

Even in her very first months of life, Old Mama felt how important Granny Mare was to the herd. She was many summers older than anyone else in the band. She knew the history of their home range. She knew how to find water in a drought and where to go to find the precious last bits of grass.

Old Mama remembered coming in to water, late one hot afternoon. The mares and foals were thirsty and anxious for the water. Golden Stallion and Granny Mare kept them back, as they searched the air for any scent of danger. Finally, they were let in to the water. How welcomed it was as they all drank their fill.

A breeze began to blow down the canyon toward the direction they had come. Suddenly it happened; a monster was among them! The band scattered, then regathered, and on a full run they were gone. But the little filly couldn't keep up. A strange, thin, snakelike thing had trapped her. First it had settled easily around her chest, and then somehow she had become wrapped in it. She was so completely trapped that for a moment she stood still, trying to figure out where the problem was coming from.

Several times that season her mama had shown her man off at a distance. Man was usually busy caring for his cattle. But now she was not only close to man, she was somehow connected to him.

He had been watching the herd's descent from the hill to the water hole. He had watched them several days in a row. He had finished his cattle work early that day and was coming by just as they entered the canyon. The wind was in his favor, blowing out of the canyon. He was mounted on a blue roan mustang he had caught on Mary's Mountain. Moving easily, they blended in with the sagebrush. He waited for them all to fill, knowing it would be easier to make a catch. It was not an accident that he caught the small, sorrel filly. She had four stocking feet and a blazed face. She showed the breeding that came from the good stock turned out onto open range during World War II. The stock was not so much turned out, as it was simply not gathered in. Being short of help, the ranchers' priorities had changed. During those difficult times, just getting the cattle cared for was oftentimes a chore. If a mare or two strayed to the wild bunch, it was just left that way.

When she found herself wound up like a kitten in a ball of yarn, Old Mama remembered she had called for her mama. But there was no answering call. There was only the man on the blue roan, the rope, and one small, sorrel filly. A hawk circling above squealed a protest. It seemed the three figures on the ground were too close to her nest.

The man on horseback came nearer and began to move in a circle around the frightened little filly. This seemed to loosen her entrapment, but her freedom dash was cut short. He was using a very long rope and he could make use of every inch of it. He would wind her in the rope, and then reverse it. With each turn of the rope he moved in closer. He was always in control. He was in control of his horse, his rope, and the little filly.

If a stranger had been watching, he might have thought the man could not control the filly so quickly, but this man was a determined one. This Determined One never thought he couldn't, so he always could. He could do just about whatever he set out to do. He planned to take the little filly home beside the blue roan, and at about sunset, he did so.

Old Mama remembered well her first hours with the Determined One. As he worked the rope around her, he talked. For pauses, exclamations and periods in his talk, he used some strange sounds. When she was very young, she had thought these were special words. Determined One used them to connect his speech, as though they had magic. As she spent more time in Man's world, Old Mama discovered these could be bad words. She heard other men use those words to abuse their horses and dogs, their wives and their children.

As the Determined One worked the rope, he moved in closer. When he was close enough to touch her, it seemed quite natural for him to do so. His touch did not seem so different from Mama's. The quiet confidence of his movements gave her confidence. She let him lead her to his home beside the blue roan.

When his family came to see the new addition, they were quiet and respectful. They realized everything was new and scary for her. They all thought she was the prettiest little thing. The Determined One said she was just about what Old Rosie's foal would have been. The one she lost last spring foaling. This little one was the same color. The main difference was this little filly had more chrome. When the papers were sent in that fall, Old Rosie's foal lived again.

The little filly's first night alone was in a 45-foot-round, willow corral. The last person she saw, just as the dark settled in, was Determined One. In the middle of the night she was aware of him. When he checked his irrigation water, he checked on her. The first light of morning, he was standing by the corral with his first cup of coffee of the day. He checked her water bucket and brought her some fresh grass-hay. She hadn't felt much like eating or drinking. He stood quietly and watched her.

As he watched the thin little filly, he could see blue ribbons at the county fair. He saw her in the winner's circle in the Snaffle Bit class. He saw her winning the Hackamore, the Two Rein and the Nevada Bridle class. He saw her as the dam and grand dam of winners. He told her she was a winner; he knew a winner when he saw one. His vision was such, he may not have seen her as a winner had she been in someone else's corral. But she was his, and she was a winner. She was a beauty. She was smart. She was athletic. She had a willing disposition. She was all those things and more.

The reason this too busy man could spend so much time just observing a tiny filly was twofold. He knew instinctively the more he presented himself to her the sooner she could begin to accept him as her world. In this difficult financial time it was a lift for him to dream about the future.

2

Determined One had decided not to put this filly with the other colts. He would keep her in the box stall in the old barn. Though it was an added chore for him, he would carry her water. He would fit her feed ration to her needs. He could tell that her mama's milk had dried up early and so had the grass. He knew he would have to play nutritional catch-up. All the early growth stages were so crucial that catch-up was hard to play. But he was a determined one and he would see her grow up fit.

After the little filly was in her new home in the old barn, she discovered what Determined already knew. It was a very busy place.

It was like being in the middle of a menagerie. Determined had always encouraged his two daughters to have animals and to care for them. They had all the critters he had enjoyed as a boy, and the ones he never had too! There were strolling-by guinea hens and strutting-by geese, banty hens with their chicks and a banty rooster that would fight anything on sight.

Added to the menagerie were many others. Jack and Jill were half-grown kids who were trouble when they could get through the barnyard fence. These little goats could make a trampoline out of the hood of the old ranch pickup. Also, in the barnyard mix was a small flock of sheep. The sheep grazed in the pasture during the day but were gathered by Dog at nightfall for lockup in the barn. The safety of the lockup prevented the sheep from becoming coyote feed during the night.

Old Mama felt she was forgetting some of the others in that barnyard but they seemed too numerous to remember.

The second day in her new home, Determined gave the pretty little filly a name. He called her Bonita. This was his name for her, all the years she lived there. She surely was a pretty one.

In her new home she had much to get acquainted with. Sheep Dog was often at the barn. He was Determined's best hand. In these lean times, he was often his only hand. For some of his work, Determined traded his labor with neighboring ranches but for much of his help he depended upon his dog. The dog helped work the cattle. He helped work the sheep. He even helped Determined with the colt breaking, but the most demanding job he had was Busy Boy.

He had just fallen into the job you might say, when Busy Boy first toddled out of the house. It was a warm, summer Sunday and Determined brought the little fellow out while his mama was frying chicken in the kitchen. The little fellow was busy exploring everything when Determined was suddenly called to the phone. Dog was dozing under the porch. Determined woke him, signaled toward the toddler and said, "Watch him." Dog watched him. Busy Boy went this way. He went that way. He went over to the corner of the big country yard. He fell into the only sizable pool of water in the shallow ditch that meandered through the yard. Dog knew that wasn't right, so he quickly grabbed Busy's denim overalls and pulled him out. Immediately, the boy put up an awful signal and everyone came running. His mama picked up the wet toddler while Determined patted Dog's head and said "Good Boy!"

From that time on, Dog had another job. It was a full time job whenever Busy was let out of the house. It became quite a challenge. Like any of his other jobs, there were rules Dog had to follow when watching after Busy Boy: no getting into water and no escape from the house yard. Dog quickly learned to place himself between the baby and any danger.

He learned that he could herd the little fellow sort of like the sheep. If the baby got too near the water or was too determined to go there, he had another tactic. He would gently push him over. Busy would just sit down on his round bottom. This was certain to make him angry, and he sure could holler. His squawking always brought reinforcements from the house.

Old Mama remembered that by the time she came to live with the family, Busy was about three-and-a-half-years old and he pretty much had the run of the ranch. Always the dog was along to get him out of trouble. He was an impulsive fellow and Dog had to play rescue quite often.

Dog was quick to intervene when Busy, unthinking, followed his ball into the corral with a tight-bagged cow. She was on the fight. Dog latched onto her tail, which got her attention. The little fellow rolled safely out under the fence.

Neither Determined nor Dog hurried to the rescue when Busy mixed it up with the Banty family. He had been told, more than once, not to try to catch the banty chicks. He followed them all morning and finally caught one. When Mama Banty flew into his face, he dropped her chick. Then Banty Rooster arrived and chased him onto the grain bin. From on top of the bin, he put up a terrible yawl, which sounded more mad, than hurt. Determined checked it out; then he and Dog had work to do down along the fence. Dog never knew if the rooster left or someone else rescued Busy Boy. But, he knew Mama Banty's chicks had a peaceful summer after that.

By the time Bonita came to live in the barnyard, it was pretty well established. Busy would never do today whatever he had done yesterday. It was difficult for Determined to make rules for his son. He really was an obedient little fellow. He did not do the things he was told not to do. But, no one knew what he would do next, not even Busy.

Bonita's introduction to Busy was quite an experience. Determined had just checked to see how she was settling into her new surroundings. He had gone to check his irrigation water. It was peaceful and quiet. All the other animals and family had treated her with consideration and respect.

Busy wandered in carrying a baling twine rope. Tom Turkey was making a dust bath over in the corner of the dirt-floored barn. Busy adjusted his loop. He took three steps, threw, and caught Tom Turkey. There were feathers and dust flying everywhere. There was squawking and hollering and all the other fowl on the place joined the fray. The little filly was terrified. Tom Turkey alighted in the rafters, trailing the twine rope. Busy sat on the barn floor dirty-faced and grinning. His sisters arrived. They wasted energy telling Busy not to rope the turkey again. He wouldn't rope old turkey again, likely he couldn't. He wouldn't think of roping that old turkey again. He hadn't thought about roping him the first time. He did think about his rope though. He hoped it would loosen up and fall off before Dad saw it. After all the dust settled and the sisters left to report to the house, Busy's attention turned to the new filly. He went outside and found a handful of grass. He came back to Bonita to make friends.

As Determined took the rope off the turkey when he was at roost that night, he thought about his father. He used to think his dad had eyes in the back of his head. He now knew the truth. The only extra eyes were in the heart. The ones that looked back and remembered being a child.

$\mathcal{3}$

A few days after the turkey incident, Bonita got another fright. It had been quiet all morning. The family had gone to town to shop for school clothes. Busy had been bribed to go along with the promise of an ice cream cone. The morning had been clear and warm. As early afternoon arrived, so did some very dark clouds. This did not disturb the little filly. She had seen other storms.

Half dozing in the sun, Old Mama could feel again that fright of years ago. There was a bright flash, then a loud rumbling roar; the wind blew leaves and branches against the barn. A terrifying pounding began overhead. She startled and ran against the wall. In a panic, she circled her tiny home. She stood trembling against the back wall. Then he was there. His shirt was wet from his dash through the hail. He came into the stall with her. How good it was to see him. He was talking and the noise didn't seem so loud. He asked her if the hail had scared her. He knew it had. Her eyes seemed to almost pop out of her head. He rubbed her and reassured her. "She was safe. She was a brave girl. She was not afraid of any old hail on a tin roof." As usual, what he had said was true. Looking back she wondered: Did he believe before he spoke, or in hearing, did he then believe?

In a few moments the hail passed but the clouds hung around. Determined figured this would be a good time to put new shoes on Smoky. Smoky was a ten-year-old grula gelding. This handsome bridle horse was his hope for prize money at the county fair. If he got Smoky to the fair looking good, folks would admire him. Standing in the winner's circle, Smoky would probably attract a moneyed buyer. By working long hours he had managed to raise a good hay crop. Cattle prices were down. If he could do well at the fair and sell a horse or two, he'd be able to keep most of his heifers. Surely prices would rebound in a year or two. He had enough fall pasture and hay to hold on, but he needed cash to make it work.

In a few minutes he was back in the barn with Smoky. Bonita watched this new activity with interest. Smoky had been shod many times before and he knew the routine. Determined was glad Busy was in town. Busy could make the most routine chore take on new adventures. Determined was determined to consider them adventures rather than problems, but at the end of a long day it could be a test.

As Determined set down Smoky's third foot, he heard the car door slam. Maybe Busy would stay busy at the house for just a little while. No such luck. He heard the barnyard gate. The little fellow was hollering, "Hey Pop," and coming along at a jog. His Pop stopped horseshoeing. He went to the open barn door to greet him. From the looks of him, he'd had more than an ice cream cone. Not only were there ice cream dribbles on his shirtfront, there was cherry sucker on his chin. There was even licorice evident on his nose. It was a good thing he didn't go to town often.

In his excitement he was stuttering. Sometimes he did that when his thoughts got ahead of his speech. The family usually just waited for the second or third telling. Given time, he could express his thoughts and feelings quite well. Old Mama remembered Determined once told her he had had something of a similar problem when he was a youngster. He wondered if having older siblings didn't contribute to that situation. He thought one reason that he talked so rapid-fire may have been his desire to be heard as a child. In a large family one may get interrupted, ignored or out-volumed pretty easily. The older ones can usually tell the story clearer and faster. They have used language longer and know how to put it together. The younger ones learn early how to have emergencies that interrupt. The fellow in the middle needs to be truly fast at everything. Determined was fast at talking, walking, working and thinking.

When Busy slowed down, Determined realized he had gotten more than eating treats at town. He had conned Grams out of a new toy gun. It was built like a shotgun. You could cock it. You could pull the trigger. It made a loud pop. It made a very loud "POP!" It looked like it was really well made. Determined wondered why!

He picked up Busy and sat him on top of the grain bin. The grain bin was a storage unit, located just inside the door of the barn, which had a very sturdy, hinged wooden top. It was well made and held about a ton of grain. Determined had formed a habit of setting Busy up there, as it was large enough for him to play comfortably and high enough to discourage him from getting off easily. Busy had grown enough this summer to get on and off; however, being tired from his town trip, he was willing to be treated as if he were younger. He sat quietly while his Dad finished putting the shoes on Smoky, hurrying to get the job done before supper time.

Just after supper the sky cleared off and the sun came out and shone bright. In the summer their breakfast, dinner and supper meals were at six, twelve, and six, but in the winter they ate at seven, twelve, and five. In Northern Nevada country the heartiest meal was in the middle of the day. Lunch was something to be carried behind the saddle or on the seat of the pickup truck. Most of the other ranches kept the same schedule. Folks who came by were always welcome to share a meal.

In the summer a lot of daylight remained after supper. This was the time for the evening chores. In the winter when the days were cold and short, the choring was usually done before supper, just about dusk.

That same night just after supper, everyone was hurrying around with their evening chores because company was coming. The kids would play together and the grownups were planning to play pinochle. In the house the fudge was already cooling on the windowsill. Determined was haying the horses he housed in various corrals. The girls were caring for their menagerie. Busy was shooting everything with his "bang gun." A bright red and white De Soto loaded with chrome pulled into the yard. It parked down near the barn. Determined's first thought was what the car would look like if Jack and Jill got to it. He hurried over to the parked car just as the owner got out. Determined was surprised to see Mr. Cattle Buyer, who was a couple of days early. He apologized and explained his early arrival. Determined didn't mind; he was prepared. The cattle Determined wanted to show him were gathered in a nearby field, on good pasture, so Determined suggested they go in the De Soto to look them over. His reasoning was half the fear of Jack and Jill's mischievous ways and half wanting just one ride in that new car. Maybe cattle buyers could drive new cars, but he couldn't imagine cattle ranchers owning one.

Determined and Cattle Buyer had both read the same article in a periodical about aviation medicine on the threshold of space. They talked about reading Buck Rogers as kids and thinking it was so far fetched. Neither could picture space exploration or even why anyone would want to explore space. It gave them something to talk about until they were ready to talk cattle prices. Prices were important down to the one-quarter cent, as was the shipping date and time. These details could dictate the profit or loss for a year of hard work. When they got back to the house, they shook hands. Determined thought he'd gotten all he could. Mr. Cattle Buyer felt he'd given all that he could live with. He was glad not everyone he dealt with could talk as fast and think as fast as this determined rancher.

As they pulled back into the yard, the dust had just settled from the arrival of the company. The cattle buyer left, going to Elko for the night. Determined's wife rushed out and ushered her lady friend into the house while Determined and his man friend lingered beside the car talking cattle prices. A rancher usually never told anyone the exact price he received. He never told anyone how many cattle he ran. Folks who knew this unwritten rule never asked. People who asked never knew about the rule. After the fact, they would realize they had never gotten an answer.

A few minutes of talk brought Determined's thoughts back to the little filly. He wanted to check on her before he went in for the night. Patting his friend on the back, he smiled and urged him to come see the new member of his ranch family.

They were talking when they came around the corner into the barn. Things were great. Then things changed. Smoky was in the door of the barn with his head in the open grain bin. Somehow, in the excitement of the cattle buyer and the company, someone had left a gate unfastened.

Smoky was a munch mouth who had taken a mind to help himself. There was no way of really knowing how long he'd been out or how much he had eaten. The men looked at Smoky, then at each other. They both realized the danger of founder, which veterinarians called laminitis, but by whichever term it was a big problem. Determined looked at his friend. His usually quick speech had slowed down. "The mineral oil is in the bathroom, top shelf of the cabinet behind the door. Don't worry the women. Just say we've a little problem. We won't be in for a while."

Determined fit a halter on Smoky and led him to the tack room where there was a light. He had some vet-type supplies and equipment in the special locked cabinet. He kept his mind away from how the horse got out and who left the grain bin open. He didn't even allow himself to think about the reason he was using rolled barley, not rolled oats. The barley had been given to him. Cash was so short he was thankful for anything he didn't have to buy.

In just a few minutes his friend was back from the house. Determined set about taking care of Smoky. Determined had been a boy during the Great Depression and a young man during World War II, with all its shortages. He knew help was what you did for yourself.

As a kid he had paid lots of attention to what the old ranchers said and did for their stock. Some of it was still pretty good practice. A few years back he had spent some time on a big spread, an outfit that could afford a vet. Determined had usually acted as the vet's assistant. They were still good friends.

His friend was younger, with less experience. He was eager to help and eager to learn. Whatever Determined asked of him, he did. After the mineral oil, they just walked Smoky quietly in the soft dirt at the edge of the corral about fifteen minutes out of every hour. The rest of the time they stood him in the running water in the little creek that ran through the barnyard. At about ten o'clock, Determined left his friend standing Smoky in the creek. He went into the house and came out with cups, a pot full of coffee and some fudge. The women and children were settling in for the night. The men spent the night outdoors tending Smoky.

Thinking back, Old Mama realized the outcome of that long night was not only that Smoky remained sound, but also Determined began to see more of the eager young friend who was so much help with Smoky. Watching from her stall she began to think of this fellow as the Eager One. It was nice to see Eager and Determined become closer friends.

Smoky went on to do well that fall at the fair and was indeed in the winner's circle. The best part of that news was after the steers shipped in the fall, Mr. Cattle Buyer came back to the ranch and bought Smoky.

After the fair, Determined was very busy during the fall, gathering cattle for himself and for the neighbors. He had less time to be around the barn, so it seemed natural for the girls to begin to include Bonita in their menagerie. When she had first come to the barnyard, she had been a special guest. Dad had told them not to bother her, but she had become accustomed to her surroundings by now and she was very seldom startled at anything.

Bonita watched the little folks come and go. She watched the grownups too. She watched them with each other; she watched them with the animals. There was something special about the small ones, though. She watched Busy crouch on his legs for over a half hour, watching a trail of ants carry off a piece of bread crust. She saw his excitement over a found feather or a shiny rock. She saw the girls' joy over Calico's nest of five baby kittens. She could share with them their wonder at the new barn life. While still growing so close to the ground, she thought the children seemed more in tune with the earth. Bonita formed a special feeling for the small ones that she kept all her life.

As she watched the girls come and go, she could tell one of them was certainly bossy. It wasn't that she actually called the shots, but she surely tried. The other was so tiny, Bonita wondered about Determined telling everyone, "This filly needs extra nutrition," when his own little girl looked like she'd been on short rations all her life. Actually, she was the older of the two, and in reality she had the lead role even though Bossy tried to direct activities. This Bitsy One was very intense, always going about the chores with an air of assurance.

Two weeks later, there was lots of excitement around the barnyard. Overnight company was coming on Saturday. The girls decided they should have a "Special Fair." They began to arrange the barn so fairgoers could see the exhibits. Bonita's stall was perfect, already in the right place. They made more partitions by dragging hay bales to form other stalls. On the day of their fair, they would confine Jack and Jill and their bucket calf in separate stalls, place the kittens in a chicken coup and some banty chicks in a cage and even put Dog on a leash.

They planned to put some young rabbits in a small cage on top of the feed bin. It was really quite an ambitious project for two small girls. They told their teacher and invited their whole school (all five pupils) to their fair on Saturday afternoon. Bitsy asked the teacher for some construction paper to make ribbons for the fair. Teacher offered red, white, and blue paper, but Bitsy only needed blue. Everyone was a winner in her eyes.

Saturday came and so did the fairgoers. All of the pens and cages had blue ribbons. Eager and his family had gotten there just in time for the chicken dinner. Bitsy could hardly spare the time to eat in her excitement over the fair. Two little boys from a neighboring ranch came with their folks just before the fair started. At the very last minute, Bitsy had gotten the okay to take Kool-Aid and brownies to the barn so she could have a food booth.

A tour of the Barn Fair didn't take long. This was followed by the horse show. All the big people sat on a bench against the barn. All the little people were contestants. Bitsy was ring steward, judge, and announcer. Some of the mounts had been Christmas gifts and were quite well put together, stocking heads on sturdy broomsticks. They had felt ears, button eyes, colorful yarn manes, and real leather reins. To fill out the classes, Bitsy, with some help from her dad, had made extra horses from sturdy tree sticks, to which she had fastened socks stuffed with straw. Her color crayons had fashioned eyes, ears, and noses. Since these events did not depend on looks, the show went quite well.

Bitsy borrowed Bossy's horse and demonstrated the reining pattern before each class. Since the cow-working section had been eliminated by Dad, the whole event went rather smoothly.

Bossy was the first to exhibit in the Snaffle Bit class. She was quite impressive; she stayed on pattern and received a good score. Eager's little girl forgot to back up but was very considerate of her horse. Then it was the boys' turn. School Friend started the boy's competition. He had a pretty good idea about the figure eights, even though he went off pattern. He tried to make up for it with his sliding stops and fast spins. Then it was Busy's turn. He came riding, circling, and spinning. Next, School Friend's little brother made a lot of dust, but no one was sure what pattern he was following. Eager's little boy's horse stumbled and had a very bad fall. Since he was the last contestant in that class, it was decided to have a Kool-Aid break.

After the break the other classes were run: Hackamore, Two Rein, and Open Bridle. The presentation of awards followed immediately after the last class. Bitsy had gone to the bottom of the toy box for the awards. Every contestant received a recycled toy to keep for his or her own. The boys got toy cars and left to make a racetrack in the tractor tire sand box. The girls received some lovely carnival jewelry. The rings were adjustable; one size fit all.

After the awards presentation, Determined and Eager helped Bitsy put things back where they belonged, and then Bitsy left to catch up with the others who had scattered. The neighbors left for a trip to town to go grocery shopping. Determined and his friend decided the barn was a good place to be, as a chill wind had started and it was threatening rain.

Eager had brought a gunny sack full of mane hair he had been collecting for months. Every time another buckaroo trimmed his horse's mane, Eager was there to save the hair. Hair mecates weren't difficult to make, but it took some work to get the hair ready. Using the bench they had just put inside, in a few minutes they were set up to pick hair.

Eager had a problem. The ranch he worked for was a big outfit. They ran almost 10,000 head of cattle and a large herd of horses. Each hand had his own string of horses. Mostly, a fellow kept the same horses year in and year out. A buckaroo had quit recently, and Eager had asked Buckaroo Boss for that rider's hackamore horse. The horse was fifteen and a half hands, seal brown, naturally active and had lots of cow. The problem facing Eager was that Brown's face was too close to his own. The previous rider had been riding him only a short time in the hackamore. The more he had worked on the head position, the more Brown elevated his head. He had worked on the position quite a lot out behind the barn and the last few sessions he had even rigged up a tie-down to use.

Determined knew the horse and he knew the rider hadn't quit his job but had been asked to leave. That is, it was suggested he might be happier somewhere else, and it was a sure thing the horses in his string would be happier without him. The man was a heavy-handed fellow whose idea of setting up a stop was to shout "Whoa" and give one big pull with both hands. He had started the brown colt in the snaffle bit. When he had trouble there, he went to the hackamore. When the horse didn't progress in a light hackamore, he had borrowed a very stiff hackamore from a friend. Although careful with the horses in his string that might buck, he was really demanding of all his other horses.

Determined suggested that Eager take Brown back to the snaffle bit. The only thing to do with him around the barn was to saddle up and leave. This season, Eager's riding was mostly pushing stragglers from the high country. Determined figured Brown was old enough and in good enough physical condition to get a lot from that sort of work. Following cattle down the trail on a loose rein wouldn't seem much like what he had been exposed to so far. Determined reminded Eager of all the chances he could have during the day to work in other lessons. The flat bottom of a dry gulch with a bank would be a good place to work on sets-and-turns.

The more they talked, the more enthused they got about Brown's potential. The high point was when Determined remembered that Heavy Hand had not started Brown. Brown had been started as a long three-year-old when the ranch had hired a really experienced older fellow who was sure enough a horseman. A couple of the younger buckaroos were teamed up with him to start about nineteen head of colts and Brown was one of those colts. They had gotten a good start in that six or seven weeks, then the colts had been turned out into the winter pasture. This news made the day for Eager. He believed, as Determined did, that the first handling was always an experience the horse remembered, good or bad. He was relieved to know the foundation had been good.

The next morning before daylight, Determined started the fire and made coffee. The kitchen range was propane but there was a wood-burning unit attached. There had been a frost that night, so the warmth felt good. Determined and Eager let the household sleep and headed for the corral.

Determined had four head of horses in the corral. These were colts he was working with, and he had spent every minute of his spare time getting them prepared for today. They had been sacked out, bitted, and saddled up, and even taught to stand hobbled. Today, with Eager's help, they were going to be ridden in the corral, and outside, if it seemed right.

One colt was a long two-year-old. Likely, he would just be gotten on and off and briefly moved around in the corral.

Two colts were past three years, and one colt Determined had traded a neighbor hay for was a nonregistered, four-year-old. Determined planned to use his blue roan and lead Eager on the colts. Everything went so well they forgot about breakfast and stayed with the colts until almost noon. Eager had to gather up his family and leave right after the noon meal because out-of-state relatives were coming to stay overnight at his home.

Determined ran a three-man outfit with just his dog. He knew how to plan his work to get those two-man projects attended to when company came. These were not surprises, they were planned activities. The younger fellows still working for the big outfits often dreamed of having their own spread someday. The advantage for riders like Eager was a chance to learn some of what Determined already knew.

Old Mama woke from her remembering; she looked around and absolutely nothing was happening. Even the flies were quiet, so she went back to her reminiscing. It was easy to think back to that time. From inside her snug stall or outside in her small run, she was pretty well able to observe all the goings on. From her observation spot inside her run, she could see the gate to Determined's round corral. The corral was a willow type but the gate was pole construction. She was the right height to see between the poles. This allowed her to observe Determined's work with the current crop of colts.

The two-year-old was a gentle, flaxie-maned sorrel colt. Determined usually just saddled him every day and let him wear the saddle for a while. The colts that were past three years took more attention. The leggy bay had found it very difficult to stand on three legs, being introduced to anything new really upset him. Bonita wondered at that. She did not figure she would be afraid of any old gunnysack or saddle blanket. She had seen scarier things than that in this barn full of adventures.

The other three-year-old was a brother to the flaxie sorrel two-year-old. He too was a sorrel, though not as flashy in color as his brother, but he did have the same gentle disposition. Sacking out was no big deal to him and learning to accept the hobbles was not a problem, either. He tested them once and when he found he couldn't walk off, he stayed in place and dozed off. It was important for a colt to learn to accept being hobbled, because no buckaroo relished the thought of walking back to camp.

The non-registered four-year-old seemed to have difficulty with each lesson. He was brown in color. This season his coat was bleached out. He was well built, so when he stopped, his hind feet slid under him naturally. When he turned, it was one motion. Though his body was beautiful, his head did not seem to belong to it. Bonita wondered what went on inside his head. He could learn to accept his hind foot being tied up. He could learn to accept the sack or saddle blanket being thrown on or around him. He could accept the hobbles, the bit, and the saddle. The problem he seemed to have was the need to challenge each new phase of the training. She wondered about him.

This season brought chilly nights. One morning, Bonita found something strange in her water bucket. Something cold and hard caused her to draw her head back from her bucket without getting her morning drink. When Determined came to feed and water her, he lifted out the cold hard sphere and tossed it outside her stall. When it hit the ground, it shattered. Later in the day there were only wet spots where it had been.

Lately, Bossy and Bitsy had only been in the barn long enough to do their chores, pet the kittens, and hurry back into the house. Sometimes they brought Bonita an apple. The apples were all picked now and sitting in baskets and boxes in the cellar. The family had not had as large a vegetable garden as they usually did because of the short water year. However, the girls had planted several hills of pumpkins, and along the fence they had grown gourds. They had more than enough for their own use and to share with everyone at school.

Early one Saturday morning, they began to decorate the barn. They had taken their very best pumpkins to the teacher. They were saving some really good ones for the real Halloween. This left them lots of smaller or strange-shaped pumpkins to carve for the barn animals. Bonita's own jack-o-lantern was a bit one-sided. Bitsy gave it character with half-moon eyes and a three-tooth grin. Bossy had smuggled a sharp knife from the kitchen. When the knife slipped and the blood came, she smuggled the knife back into the kitchen. The girls decided to bag that part of the project. They finished decorating by using their crayons to give the gourds and pumpkins character.

Bonita had been a barn resident long enough to recognize from all the extra activity that something special was happening. From all the preparation it looked like company might be coming. Bonita was right about that. Eager and his family arrived in midafternoon.

Immediately, all the children made a tour of the barnyard. They were really excited about Halloween. There was to be a school carnival that evening after supper. Bitsy and Bossy eagerly told their company all the things in store for them. Set up at the school was a ringtoss booth, a fishpond, a fortune-teller with a crystal ball, a beanbag throw to knock off the witch's hat, and a very scary spook house. There was to be a food booth serving big juicy hot dogs, orange popcorn balls, sweet-smelling caramel apples, fresh brownies and punch or coffee.

Eager and Determined were almost as excited to be together again as the children. Eager had brought his saddle. In just a few minutes he and Determined were mounted and leaving the corral on the two three-year old colts. Their plan was to get the work finished early. The flaxie sorrel would only require a little quality attention in the corral today. Determined had worked with the brown colt, Pete, before the noon meal. By finishing early, everyone could get to the schoolhouse in time for the fun.

5

Old Mama remembered she was still dozing in her stall when she heard Determined and Eager close the backdoor of the house. It was the morning after the Halloween party. Eager needed to leave early for home. When the days grew shorter and the nights colder, the cattle headed down to the home ranch and winter feed. The last stragglers were coming out of the high country. It was Eager's job to ride the water gaps. Whenever he found cattle at a water gap, he would open the gate and drive them into the field where there was still old feed. The cattle would be held there until the numbers were large enough, and then they would be driven toward their winter feed ground on the part of the ranch that was down along the Humboldt River.

Since Eager would be leaving early, the fellows were in a hurry to start the day. They really were anxious to spend time together with the colts. Eager was having trouble with the colts in his string, keeping the head position he wanted when he backed up. He had been watching Determined who didn't seem to have that problem, and Eager wanted to learn his technique.

The morning was warmer than it had been a week ago. That made it easier for things to come alive earlier. Bonita could hear the other horses chomping down their breakfast but she wasn't hungry yet. She was more curious to watch Eager and Determined who were now making odd noises in the tack room. They were repairing some gear and mucking out the mess.

Determined kept a pretty tidy tack room but sometimes after a really busy season of work, it needed attention. Eager was still, you might say, in the apprentice stage. This desire to learn even included making and repairing gear. The tack room project and the horses' breakfast finished about the same time.

They saddled the long-legged bay and the gentle-natured sorrel. They were bitted and left checked up for a few minutes. The smell of coffee and bacon drew the fellows back into the kitchen. Since these fellows were the eat-and-run variety, they were back at the corral in no time. Eager's saddle was on the bay colt. Determined was riding the sorrel. First they moved the colts around in the corral. Then they caught them, reset their saddles, mounted, and left the barn area. They had a little project moving some cattle from one field to another. Riding out and back would give them the chance to talk about and explore Eager's problem. They decided Eager could have more success by using lighter pulls and slacks with first one rein and then the other. A rider could pull both reins evenly and get results, too. Probably, what was causing the most trouble was expecting too much too soon. By the time they got back from moving the cattle, Eager had a lot to think about on his way home.

After about a week of beautiful weather, it turned cold again. Bonita noticed that all the pretty leaves were now scattered on the ground. Some of them blew into her run, and they made a crackling noise when she walked among them.

With this sharper change in the weather, the little people only came to the barn at chore time. One day they decorated her stall with construction paper pilgrims and colorful turkeys drawn on a hand outline and colored brightly.

The moon had gone from full to only a sliver and then back to full again by the next time Eager and his family came. The daylight shortened every day. Determined had turned the three youngest colts back out into winter pasture. He was only working with his "trade colt." Pete was older and needed to have more time spent with him. Determined didn't consider him a problem horse, but he wasn't a horse that seemed to remember very well. Determined continued Pete's training by keeping him in a pen in the barnyard and working with him every day. Some days he took him for quite long rides, looking for late fall strays. Some days there was only time to saddle and bit Pete and check him up in the round corral. When checking Pete up, he always made sure one rein was a little shorter than the other and that there was enough slack so that when Pete tucked his nose, he would feel a little slack.

The Saturday after Turkey Day, when Eager and his family came to visit, it was cold and starting to snow. Determined saddled Pete, checked him up in the round corral, and then Determined and Eager went to the barn to twist horsehair mecates. They were enjoying the work but interrupted themselves before very long to unsaddle Pete and return him to his corral. Determined explained to Eager the importance of not leaving Pete checked up too long. He felt it was another training method that could easily be overdone.

The weather had warmed up considerably after the snow began to fall. As Determined and Eager twisted the strands for the new mecate, they talked about the how and when to double a horse. The horses in Eager's string were at opposite ends of ability when it came to sliding and turning back. The older hackamore horses, which had been given to him when he signed on, were all quite handy. With only a light pull on the reins, they would slide to a stop. With a light pull to the side on a single rein, they would turn halfway around with their front feet off the ground. He noticed this mostly in the corral, working cattle. He didn't do much set-and-turn stuff except during natural work. He knew he needed to develop this same, easy action with his younger colts.

Determined suggested turning his younger horses against an obstacle, such as a solid board fence, so the horse would have to turn short. Then, a light pull on a single rein would make the horse come around with the front feet off the ground. Determined cautioned Eager not to hang onto the rein after his horse started to turn. Determined rode with tapederos and could use them to spook his colts into hurrying on through the turn-back until they understood how to put it together.

Eager's stirrups had tapederos and he considered them valuable as a way to keep his feet protected. He had always before thought the longer tapederos seemed overdone, but he began to see some value in the longer version when riding his colts.

By the time the evening meal was ready, the men had finished one really nice mecate. Eager had confided to Determined his dream of leaving this area of harsh winters. Although he had never been there, he had heard a lot about California.

Bonita had spent the afternoon watching Determined and Eager put the mecate together, as they shared their knowledge of horses, building on their friendship. Since the little folks didn't play in the barn much in the colder weather, it was a treat for Bonita to have so much company.

The snow that came that weekend stayed on the frozen ground. Every few days another snowstorm came. Soon it was necessary to use the equipment to plow out and pack down the roads and driveways. Determined began to feed the cattle using the workhorses to pull the sled. When he had bought the ranch a few years back, four head of work horses had come with the outfit, as had quite a bit of equipment to use with horses. In his struggle to keep expenses down, Determined had found these horses to be an advantage.

Bonita noticed that each day there was a shorter time of daylight. She was comfortable in her little stall inside the barn. Each day had grown colder, and she had grown quite a furry coat to keep her warm. As the ground had frozen up, so had much of the activity around the barnyard. For Bonita winter was a quiet, peaceful time.

Near the day of the least daylight, Bonita realized the children seemed to be getting excited. They spent more time in the barnyard decorating for a big holiday. One day, she heard Bitsy explaining to Bossy that this birthday celebration was the very most important of all. They were all going to celebrate "Baby Jesus' Birthday." There were to be parties with lots of decorations and gifts would be exchanged. As the special day neared, a small, potted sagebrush appeared outside Bonita's stall. It was splendidly prepared with chains of construction paper, ring streamers, and a paper mache angel on top.

The family received a card from Eager's family with the Nativity scene on the front. The note inside confirmed they were going out-of-state to spend the holiday with grandparents. Eager's family would be coming to visit between the birthday of Jesus and the first day of the New Year.

Christmas was a wonderful time for Determined's household. All in the family had been saving for months to buy the little treasures they would be wrapping in secret to place beneath the tree. They had painstakingly handcrafted other gifts in the long winter evenings. Everything was so special and so secret.

Determined usually waited well into December to go cut the tree. Normally by then, there would be enough snow to use the team and sled. The tree-cutting day was an exciting, family time for the children. Friends and neighbors were always invited along. Once the tree was home and set up in the corner, the real anticipation would begin.

Bitsy had finished early and her gifts were wrapped even before Thanksgiving. This really worked out well as it gave her time to help both Bossy and Busy. She had helped Busy to buy a new blue bandana for Determined. She helped him wrap it and print his name. He had enough change left for a miniature, china tea set. Secretly, he told the clerk he needed two of these. He had carried them home carefully and wrapped them himself. He had only shared that secret with Bonita. She had been privileged to hear about many gifts the family would be giving. She had even seen the paper doll set Bossy had drawn, colored, and carefully cut out for Bitsy.

Christmas week was made special by the program at school. At the close of the program, Santa came and everyone was given a bag with candy, nuts, and an orange. An orange was a real treat this time of year. Later in the week, Determined's cousin in town had all the family over for an afternoon feast. That evening they all went for a special pageant at the church. After each wonderful new event, one or the other of the children came to the barn to tell Bonita all about it. Sometimes they all told the same story.

The days between Christmas and the New Year brought very clear, cold nights. The days were clear with no new snow and, without wind, the days seemed warmer. This weather pattern allowed the children to spend more time out-of-doors with their new sled. With time off from school, the little people spent more time in the barn. When the house seemed too confining, they came out to the barn to build forts and carry on the great adventures of pioneer days.

Eager and his family visited that weekend. The weather cooperated to make the time a nice winter break. After the cattle were fed and the other chores taken care of, Bonita had company in the barn. Determined and Eager found time to twist a second mecate. They made this one smaller around, only about one-half inch in diameter, as Determined wanted to use it for putting the blue roan into the two-rein. He was planning to begin bridling Blue in the spring with the nice little bosal he had gotten as a Christmas gift and the new mecate. They used mostly mane hair, but added a little tail hair. Because they had used all the sorrel hair on their first hair rope, this mecate was salt and pepper and Determined thought it would look fine on Blue.

Blue would be six-years-old in the spring. He had been

well started in the snaffle bit and ridden over a year in the hackamore. He had even won the hackamore class at the county fair this past fall. After he had been used for the fall gathering and helping start the colts, Determined had pulled his shoes and turned him out in the horse pasture for a well earned and much needed rest.

When they finished the mecate, Determined showed Eager the Garcia spade bit he had been given years ago by an old buckaroo. It was one of Determined's most prized possessions. He would be using that bit, along with the bosal and mecate for the two-rein for Blue.

The visiting in the barn was cut short by a visit from Bitsy. She came to remind her dad of the plans for the evening. There was to be a dance at the schoolhouse. Both Determined's and Eager's wives loved to dance. The preschool children were staying at home with Aunt Martha who was also visiting over the weekend. The girls and grownups were going to the dance. They would be doing the modern dances, but they would also do the "Virginia Reel," "Put Your Little Foot Down," and "Cotton-Eyed Joe." Bitsy liked best to do the fast polkas with her dad. It was a good way to start the New Year!

6

The morning after the schoolhouse dance, the radio weatherman warned of an approaching storm. Eager volunteered to help feed Determined's stock. Since the storm was not predicted until early afternoon, Eager and his family would have time to get home. Now that it was winter and all the cattle were out of the hills, Eager lived at the home ranch close to a main-traveled highway. Still, there was always some danger in a violent storm.

Bonita didn't know about the coming storm; she sensed something was expected, but had no way of anticipating what happened next. The small door in the end of the barn crashed open and a big man staggered in. He made a few steps toward the stack of baled hay. He teetered uncertainly, then his knees seemed to give way and he came down and stayed still.

Almost at that same instant, the barn door creaked open and Bossy came in leading the way for Eager's little girl. Bossy was enjoying the morning. She really liked to have a playmate to be in charge of, but the sight of the still body by the hay bales was more than either little girl was prepared for. One scared look and they fled the area. As they hastily exited the barn, they ran into Bitsy. Bossy excitedly told her sister about the "Dead Stranger" on the barn floor. Bitsy pushed past the other girls and went to see for herself. They followed a few steps behind her.

Bitsy was only just inside the barn when she recognized the body. "It's Hoss. He worked here haying last summer."

She hurried toward the body and bent down to listen for his breath. She quickly rose up and stepped back with a wrinkled-up nose. She announced, "He's not dead, he's drunk." Before Bitsy had to take any more responsibility for the situation, she heard the feed sled coming back to the barn area. She sent Bossy and her companion for Dad.

In just moments, Determined was beside Bitsy. He had left Eager to care for the team. He sent Bossy and Eager's little girl to the house to play with the little boys and make sure they stayed in the house. Now he asked Bitsy to hurry to the house and ask for some old bedding to use in the bunkhouse. When Determined had bought the spread, the sturdy railroad tie bunkhouse was still in use. Since Determined could not afford help, it was seldom occupied now, although when Hoss had been around last summer, he had used the bunkhouse. But, when Hoss had been around last summer, he was on the wagon. He was a hard worker, clean about his person and careful about his vocabulary. There just wasn't anything in and about a ranch he couldn't do. Busy had followed him every chance he had. Hoss was considerate, kind and careful with the children. Determined and Hoss went back a long way. As young buckaroos, they had worked on the same big outfits, shared the bunkhouse, cow camp and trail.

Bonita sensed Determined's anguish and pain as he studied his friend sprawled in the dirt and hay on the barn floor. When Eager came in, he asked him to get a pot of coffee and a tin cup from the kitchen, to check out the bunk house, and start the oil heater.

Hoss was a big fellow who stood 6' 2" and had weighed 237 pounds the previous summer in bale-bucking shape. If they could get it done, Determined wanted to rouse him and get some coffee down him. If they could get him somewhat mobile, it would be easier to walk him from the barn to the bunkhouse. Eager was a hustler and in no time at all he was back with the coffee. The two of them managed to move Hoss to an upright position with his back against a bale of hay.

Determined was as patient with Hoss as if he were a child. Hoss didn't seem to know where he was or what they wanted of him, but he tried to cooperate. Between sips of coffee, Determined talked to him. He talked of past times, old times, good times. He tried to will him awake and into his world. Finally, Hoss's eyes focused on Determined's face in recognition. He half raised his right arm and pleaded, "Help me, friend!" Determined's eyes filled with tears as he whispered, "I wish to God I could!"

In a short while, they had him on his feet after a fashion. With his rubber legs and the snow on the ground, they were thankful the bunkhouse was pretty near the barn. They intended to deposit him safely on the bed, so he could sleep off this stage of his problem.

Once inside the bunkhouse, they sat for a while watching for any other problems. Eager could tell Determined was having a difficult time. Finally, he started to talk. "You know," he said, "this disease is like a viper, a huge snake that gets ahold of a person and squeezes out all the life in the mind, the body, heart and spirit. I'm his friend and I want to help, but wherever I pull the thing loose, it just coils back somewhere else. Help is just temporary. He's my friend, but I can't fight this for him. Only he can render it harmless. I guess the ones who shake this snake don't fight, they surrender and then the viper loses power."

After awhile, Determined decided Hoss could safely sleep it off, and Eager needed to get his family home before the storm hit.

The storm was late coming. It didn't arrive until after dark, but it came with more force than expected and stayed longer than anticipated. It was still a near blizzard at daylight the next day.

In late morning it cleared for a spell. Determined was

prepared for the possibility of a heavy storm. He had kept an old World War II-vintage, Power Wagon in running condition in the shop. The Power Wagon had a winch on the front. If necessary, it could be moved along the power line by using the winch to pull it from pole to pole.

Determined had been feeding the cattle progressively closer to the house. Now, they were in the house field where there was a haystack yard. Several years back, the loose hay had been stacked there with a horse-drawn operation and then later fenced off. The two stacks had settled until they were not very high, but there was still a lot of nutritious feed in them.

Determined took the Power Wagon, fencing equipment, and shovel. He took down the stackyard fence, shoveled off some snow and exposed the hay for the cattle to eat freely between heavy storms. He had saved these stacks for just such an emergency.

He wished Hoss had been able to give him a hand but he had already checked on him. Hoss would not be well enough for much activity for several days.

The day after the storm cleared out, Determined took the grocery list and went to town. He didn't want his household to be without supplies during the winter storms and more were expected. The other reason for the town trip was because he was on a quest. Hoss had gotten to his house with only the clothes on his back, and they were scant for the weather. Determined knew somewhere behind him, Hoss had left all his belongings. Sometimes belongings just disappear or are left for bar bills or room rent. Since Determined had no money to replace even a jacket and pair of gloves, he was damn determined to find Hoss's own things.

In a sleazy, across-the-tracks bar, he found Hoss's bedroll and duffel bag. The bedroll and duffel bag were still heavy, so he felt sure they had not been rifled and relieved of Hoss's gun and knife collection. The barkeep started a story about a bar tab, but one look at the jut of Determined's chin caused him to shrug and change the subject.

From the bar, Determined went to the Bed Bug Hotel and at the clerk's desk he found the rest of his friend's belongings. There was one night's room rent due and he did pay that.

He felt a little less angry on the way home.

When Hoss began to feel alive, he got acquainted with all the activities in and about the ranch. Bonita especially liked to have him come visit. One afternoon when he was in her little stall rubbing her back and visiting with her, Determined came in. Determined knew his friend had a gift of communication with animals, maybe even with everything. Something about his presence made the good days better and the bad days not so bad.

Now that he was well again had his own belongings and gear, they needed to talk about what next. Before Determined could bring up the subject, Hoss came out with a plan. He knew Determined had no money for hired help. He also knew Determined could sure use some help around the place. Hoss asked Determined, "How about I stay awhile? Think I could earn my groceries? Good trapping weather! I am a good trapper. Help you! Help me. What you think?"

Determined was relieved. It was decided. They left the barn to check out the traps in the shed. It had been so cold for so long, pelts should be prime.

Looking back, Old Mama could see again that morning, not long after Hoss came, when she woke to an unusual quiet. She wandered out into her tiny run. She couldn't quite take in the change in her world. Every branch on every tree and bush, every board, post and wire, everything, everywhere was coated with a sparkling splendor. Hoss stood like a statue outside the bunkhouse door taking in the wonder. He fell in step beside Determined as he came by on his way to the barn. "Did you ever see such a hoarfrost," he asked? Crystals of frost were floating through the air. Bonita could see the children coming out of the house and heard their excitement.

Hoss's coming seemed to change even the weather. There were many more storms that winter, but they seemed to slide in during the night, pile up the snow, and be gone in the morning. The frantic winds of the previous months weren't seen again that winter. Calmness and beauty reigned.

Eager and his family came to visit just before Valentine's Day. With a little help from Hoss, Bitsy and Bossy had decorated Bonita's stall with red and white crepe paper streamers and construction paper hearts.

The area 4-H Club was having a fund-raiser at the schoolhouse. There was to be an old fashioned box social and everybody was going. The women and girls each packed a good meal inside a fancy, decorated box that would then be auctioned off. Whoever bought the box ate the meal with the one who had prepared it.

Bitsy and Bossy had both made a box packed with fried

chicken and all sorts of good food. That night at the auction their boxes were the two highest sellers. They both ate with Hoss.

This visit, Eager brought along a bit project on which he was working. He wanted to show Determined the pattern. He had questions about the cricket he was putting into the mouth-piece. The outfit Eager worked for encouraged the Buckaroos to make their own gear. They let them use the company shop and even furnished them with sheet silver to inlay their bits and spurs.

In the past Hoss had made bits for a good part of his income. He had had quite a reputation for the quality of his work. He hadn't done much lately but he had a lot of knowl-edge to add. Digging around in Determined's shop, they found lots of things to turn into bits or spurs. Eager promised on his next visit to bring patterns of the things different fellows were working on at the ranch.

Bonita didn't see much of Eager that visit, as the fellows spent all their time in the shop. With the big people out of sight in the shop, the little people rearranged the inside of the barn and rewrote history. There were good guys shooting robbers from hay bale bank roofs and all sorts of excitement. Then Busy ran into the wheelbarrow and got an "ouyee," and Bossy got a splinter from her gun handle. The little people went to the house for first aid and food.

Bonita liked to watch the little people; they could sure make a lot of strange sounds. This time it was quiet and rest-ful when they left.

Soon, she heard the sounds of Eager's family getting ready to drive away. This time they were leaving with promises from Determined's family to come visit overnight with them for St. Patrick's Day. With Hoss on the place to care for every-thing, they could be gone for an overnight.

Hoss had done better at the trapping than either he or Determined had expected. When he had gotten his belongings back, he had discovered some greenbacks he had hidden from himself. He wasn't as broke as he thought he was so he wouldn't need to sell his pelts until the end of the season.

After Eager's visit, both Hoss and Determined were encouraged to work in the shop. Determined could see a good bit as trading material. Not all his neighbors made their own bits, but most of them had a brood mare or two. He was always ready to trade for the right kind of colt. Hoss began to see another way to make wages after the trapping season. He really didn't want to leave.

Bonita's future held changes too. Determined's plan for her in the spring was to go with the other foals to the colt pasture. He had kept her in all winter on good rations, in hopes she would catch up from her short feed start in life. He knew the colt pasture would have good feed in the spring, as the moisture content was high in the snow this year.

The snow began to disappear and soon patches of brown seemed to grow on the hillside. The brown patches stretched wider to meet each other, leaving little drifts of white accents. The days grew longer and warmer. Bonita nibbled on the tiny new grass along the edge of her run.

Hoss stayed on and calmness stayed on the ranch. He fixed things before they broke. He fed before there was hunger. When he scratched Bonita, much to her pleasure, she wondered how he knew before she knew how much she would enjoy it.

As the weather warmed and the daylight lengthened, the trapping phased out and Hoss's bit and spur business took off. The space and material were already there and a hardworking artisan was on the job. Determined added the missing ingredient to a successful business venture. He had always been a persuasive sales person. As a kid in his hometown, folks had said of him, "He could sell ice to Eskimos!"

With Hoss's help on the ranch, Determined had a little more time to be off the ranch. He went to livestock sales, cattlemen's meetings, farm implement auctions, and lots of other exciting places. He went where there were gatherings of folks from whom he could take orders for bits and spurs. As he went about looking for business for Hoss, he was alert for opportunities to trade into more stock for himself. With his ability to train horses, he could work a trade colt into good cash later in the year. Feed wouldn't be a problem for him this year, but time was his most limiting commodity. In countless ways each day, Hoss gave him the gift of time. Determined began to see he would have time enough to start some outside colts and soon other ranchers were bringing him their colts to start.

Even with all the extra activity, the calmness stayed like a warm, fuzzy blanket over the ranch. Bonita thought of Hoss, not as the Calm One, but as the Calming One. His specialness seemed to be his now ness. He never seemed to be hurrying off to somewhere nor lingering in some past place or state. He was like the children, only so much more so. It was as if he had been a child, then he had grown up and up, yet he remained a child. He was old and young beyond his years. He knew nature in a naturalness that made it seem he was of nature.

The first weekend after the corrals dried out, Determined planned to really get a jump on the colt-breaking. Eager wasn't the only one bringing his saddle. One of the single fellows from where Eager worked was coming along too. A couple other guys from another big spread planned to be there, as well as some high school kids from town who wanted to learn by watching. It would be standing-room-only around the outside of the round corral.

Determined was a showman who could put on quite a show. He was what folks referred to as a pretty forked fellow. It was okay by him if a colt had a little spook (or quite a lot of spook) left in him during the first rides. He would put the spook to use for him, getting the colts to begin to respond to his body. It was natural for Determined to ride a balance. His body worked with the horses, not against them. In that delicate duet, he was the leader. He could use his quirt, his spurs, or his thirty-inch tapederos to create momentum and be ready to make use of it.

Each time Eager came to visit, it was obvious he was becoming more anxious to explore California, and shortly after the colt breaking weekend, Determined heard that Eager and his wife had left their young ones with grandparents and gone to California to see about a job. The next time Eager's family came to visit, the car was packed full and the trailer they were towing held all the rest of their belongings. Determined felt they were making a mistake to move so far from friends and family. He probably already knew, but he had to ask what the grandparents thought of the move. Eager had expected the maternal grandparents' resistance, but he had been taken aback by his own dad's objections. Eager felt he was being responsible. He had a job with a decent wage, a decent house, and meat and milk furnished. The ranch hired other families and the school bus stopped right near the house. He was eager to go and so they went.

Before they left, Eager's family told Bonita good-bye. This was also the weekend Bonita would be leaving her winter home. Determined turned her in a small outside corral with another gentle-natured yearling. This was her first step toward becoming one of the regular yearlings in the colt pasture. When Determined fit the small halter on Bonita and led her to her new temporary home, it confirmed what he already suspected; in his time spent with her, Hoss had been doing more than scratching Bonita.

Hoss had been watching his friend catch and lead the filly, but as Determined led the little filly by Hoss, he became very busy not watching. When the space between them became the closest, Determined said, "You earned your groceries." Hoss watched his two friends walk on. He was pleased.

The other yearlings that were to share the colt pasture had all been halter-broke as weanlings. Determined had spent time working around them to be able to pick up their feet. The idea was if any of the colts needed extra care they would handle enough to accept help. In the few days before they went to pasture, Hoss and Determined gave them a refresher course.

One evening early in the week, Hoss and Determined fired up the old Power Wagon and went to check the colt pasture. The face of the small field that was the colt pasture bordered the road to town. The back of the little pasture ran up onto the hill, then across a meadow with a small creek. They discovered a couple of places where the fence needed mending before the colts were turned out. Hoss volunteered to get that job done the next day.

They decided to put all the yearlings in the vet pen the next day. The vet pen was a small lot that connected the irrigated fields to the corral setup. It was used for any project that needed space but was close enough to watch well. It was time for Babe to get acquainted with the yearlings. Babe was a pensioner that had come with the ranch. She was an older mare and had been a special mount for the lady of the house. When the property changed hands, the lady's concern for Babe was so acute, Determined volunteered to give Babe a home as long as she lived. Babe made a wonderful babysitter for children learning to ride, as well as the young pasture colts.

8

After the colts went to pasture either Determined or Hoss checked them daily. Just in the course of their everyday work, one or the other would go by the colt pasture. All they needed to do was park outside the gate, and Bonita would come to a whistle. Bonita liked being one of the colts and dashing about the pasture. Sometimes they would all dash past Old Babe, acting wild and free, but still Bonita liked visiting with "her people."

The fifteenth of June, Hoss went onto the ranch payroll. Determined's budget included about two-and-one-half months of paid help for the irrigation and the haying season. Determined was thankful he had Hoss to help, because it gave him evenings free to work with his horses.

After Eager left the spread where he had been working, Determined worked a trade. He traded Pete who really was gentle for the seal brown hackamore horse Eager had had in his string neither horse was registered. No one had really ever gotten much out of the brown hackamore horse. Determined renamed him "Pard," as he was determined they could work together and become partners. He knew the colt had the moves if he could just get together with him. In mid-June, he brought in the gentle sorrel and the leggy bay, both having matured since the previous fall. They were his hopes for the Snaffle Bit class at the fair in the fall.

Determined didn't neglect the cattle or other crops, but he needed always to make time for the horses. They were such a part of him and they really were his cash crops.

Fourth of July came and passed. The family had a little picnic in the yard, an evening with Roman candles and sparklers. Hoss was part of the family and seemed to enjoy himself, but everyone knew this could be a difficult time for Hoss. Determined knew alcoholics often fell off the wagon at holidays, anniversaries and such, but thankfully this time there was no sign of The Viper.

The Sunday evening after Independence Day, Hoss and Determined took the Power Wagon up to the colt field. They drove about for a while looking things over. Bonita was standing with them near the gate, getting the scratching from Hoss she so much enjoyed. Determined knew something was not right when they saw the ranch pickup coming, being driven by one of the high school kids, who had come to work in the haying. The message was for Hoss. His cousin had been killed in a car wreck. Back at the bunkhouse, he packed only his small bag. He gave Determined most of his bankroll to keep for him, but he couldn't meet Determined's eyes when he said, "I'll be back Thursday." That week didn't have a Thursday. There was no Thursday the next week either. There was a void on the ranch and everyone kept trying not to fall into the emptiness.

On Saturday evening, the haying crew went to town. When they came back Sunday, Hoss was with them. It was a full week until he felt well again. A certain quietness stayed with him for several weeks. One night in August, he asked Determined if he could use the Power Wagon to go to town. It was hard for Determined, but he gassed it up and gave Hoss the keys.

As he handed the keys to Hoss, he shook his hand and looked him squarely in the eyes for a moment. It was not an "everything's fine" sort of look. Somehow it was more of an "I'm here, whatever happens" kind of expression. Hoss left for town.

It was a warm August night. When all the work was finished and all the colts cooled out and put away, Determined sat on the back porch step. He watched a falling star and thought about wishing on a falling star when he was a child. He knew if he were going to wish, what that wish would be. Just as he finished that thought, the lights of the Power Wagon swung around the curve coming from town. He rolled his cigarette and lit it. He sat quietly.

After Hoss parked the Power Wagon, he went directly to the bunkhouse but before he turned the knob to go in, he saw the cigarette glow from the porch. He followed the glow and sat down beside Determined. It was some time before he spoke.

"I go to a meeting in a church basement! When I left, I don't know if I can go. You—my friend—you trusted me, then I trusted me."

Determined passed him his cigarette. Hoss took a long drag and passed it back.

"Hard day tomorrow."

"Good night."

The next two weeks were long, with lots of work for everyone. The cattle were being gathered to ship. Determined needed to be gone to help the neighbors and to gather his fat stock. As the last of the hay was brought from the meadows and stacked, he tried to put irrigation water back on the fields, so there would be more fall pasture. These were also the last weeks of preparation for the horse show at the county fair. Determined was taking two Snaffle Bit class colts, Pard for the Hackamore class, Blue Roan for the Two Rein class, and he had a bridle horse he was riding for another owner. They all needed real quality riding time just now. Even the long daylight days didn't have enough hours. During this busy time, their check of the colt pasture became a drive-by.

On the Sunday afternoon before the fair was to start, Hoss and Determined found time to take the Power Wagon up to the colt pasture. In this season of dry hot weather, the hillsides had gotten quite hard. The deer flies were pesky nearer the creek edges, so the horses spent more time out on the hill. When the Power Wagon came into sight, Old Babe and all the colts came to greet it. Bonita, who was usually first, was last. She was favoring her right front foot. Hoss, who was watching closely, thought that just maybe she favored it more after Determined began to examine it and to console her. The problem seemed to be that a small chunk had broken out of the hoof wall. The dryness of the season and the rocky hillside contributed, but Determined felt guilty he had not watched the colts more closely.

Hoss realized his friend's concern. He volunteered to walk and lead the filly home. They would travel on the softer ground near the creek. Back at the barn, Bonita went into her little stall, the one she had lived in when she first came to the ranch about a year earlier. Hoss was glad to help his friend. He realized Determined's concern, but as he had led the filly and after he closely examined the hoof, he hadn't felt it was a very serious problem yet. While Determined was riding his fair horses, Hoss trimmed the little filly's feet. When the fair horses were put away, Determined came with a booster of tetanus toxoid and an antibiotic shot. Since Determined was keeping more horses in and around the barns, Hoss noticed there were more vet supplies. When the horses went in to the fair, Determined would be spending time in town. It was decided Hoss would stay pretty close to the ranch, but he went each week to the church basement meetings.

Determined had heard from mutual friends that Eager and his family were coming to visit during the fair. He was anxious to hear what they thought of their new home.

In the summer weather, Eager liked to drive at night. They made the little folks as comfortable as they could and put the miles behind them. Just at daylight on the day before Determined was to take the horses to town, Eager and his family drove in.

After breakfast, Eager joined Hoss and Determined in

the last minute preparations for the fair. They had horses to wash and gear to clean and to pack. When there was a short break from being so busy, Eager and Determined went to see Bonita. Eager was surprised to see how much she had grown. As they stood there visiting, Determined asked if he had found the move to be the way he had it pictured. That answer was a yes and a no. The wages were fine and were paid on time. The housing included a nice yard and a place for a garden. He couldn't believe how things grew or imagine how many zucchini grew on one plant! Having close neighbors probably was fine for the family, but it sure took getting used to.

The ranch was one of the larger ones around there. Everything was cared for and kept up. It was picture postcard pretty. There were hills of oak, acres of lush pastures dotted with white-faced red cattle, and miles of white fences. (Maybe it was the fences that were making him feel closed in). He went on to tell about the horse shows and the horsemen he had met. In that area there were still quite a few older fellows who really prided themselves on their horses. They rode in the tradition of the early Spanish California Vaqueros. They were willing to expend the extra time and patience it took to make a finished reining horse. First, they had taken the time and patience to learn the ways handed down, then they took the time to put these ways into practice. Eager said he was learning everything he could from them, even though there seemed to be some secretness about it. It was all so interesting. There was pretty much a tradition to everything from the formation of the buttons on their rawhide reins to their handmade bridle chains.

However, he had found something else he was uneasy about. He had seen other riders with fast methods and different equipment. They didn't seem to have much time or patience. The horse was just another tool of their trade. They were getting rewards. The crowds applauded them. Judges placed them in the winning circle. They were becoming an elite group, like gods—Horse Gods.

Determined asked no more of his friend. He could see Eager was just as eager as ever, but now maybe he longed to go from forward to back. He wondered if his friend would ever find what he was searching for.

It was picnic weather and just before noon, the three little girls came to the barn bringing sandwiches, fruit, and lemonade. This gave the girls an important role in the fair preparations. All three men thanked them but Hoss especially made a fuss over their "cooking." The girls shared the lunch and the August issue of the *National Geographic*. There was an article about "Operation Deep Freeze." Lots of pictures were taken in the Antarctic, and the pictures of ice and snow were extra enjoyable on such a warm day. All the children liked that magazine.... even the ones who couldn't read the words loved to read the pictures.

As the fellows shared lunch, they talked about whom they might see at the fair. They mentioned their friend from up north who would likely be there. He was a real dependable sort. He had gone away to the service in World War II, gone in just a buckaroo but had come out an officer. He was dependable all right.

With all the extra help, the preparations for the fair were finished by early afternoon, and Eager's family loaded up and left to stay over with friends in town.

Bonita missed the family; it was so quiet around the barnyard with them gone, Hoss sensed this and gave her some extra scratching. Her foot was fine, but he didn't return her to the hill pasture. Soon enough, the other colts and Old Babe would be coming in to the meadow.

The family was having fun at the fair. The girls had taken their homemade cookies to compete in the cooking contest. Bitsy had painted a picture to enter in the Arts Exhibit Building competition.

On Monday evening, everyone came home in a flurry of activity. Determined had two less horses. He had sold the gentle sorrel, upon which he had placed fourth in the Snaffle Bit class. Determined had taken a third on the long-legged bay colt, which had grown into himself this season and was a tough kind of a colt. Determined called him Rawhide. He would be his hope for the Hackamore class next season. Determined and this year's Hackamore class horse had picked up a second. Blue Roan had performed beautifully in the Two-Reined class and had won the blue ribbon by several points. The bridle horse Determined had been working with placed second in the Nevada Bridle class and won first in the Open class. He had gone home from the fair with his owner.

The fair was history. Determined and his horses had brought home their share of awards. Bitsy got "Best of Show" in her age group for her artwork and both girls received blue ribbons and prize monies for their cookies.

Awards and prize money weren't the only things they brought back from the fair. Rawhide brought back distemper. This wasn't the first time they had brought distemper home after the fair either. Determined braced himself for the disease to go through all the younger horses on the place. It did just that. One by one, or two at a time, they came down with coughs, runny noses, and abscesses. They were in good flesh when they got sick. They swelled; they broke and ran, and got better, all but Bonita, who was the last to get the dreaded disease.

9

Thinking back after all the years, Old Mama could feel again her turn with the distemper. All the other colts and younger horses had a bout with it but none of them got very sick. For her, the only thing good about it was she never got it again.

Early one morning, as Bonita woke to the sound of Determined starting his truck, she felt strangely hot. When Hoss fed that morning she didn't feel like eating or drinking. By evening feeding time, she felt even worse. She stayed hot and miserable, then a strange swelling began under her jaw and yellowish yuck began to drain from her nose. She didn't want to eat or drink and rest was not restful. Hoss came to feed her and tried to scratch and console her. She stood with her neck extended, to try to get air; her nose was running and the swelling was growing. Determined knew Bonita would do best if the disease progressed on its own, but he felt so sorry for this special colt. He worried and watched. Carefully he would feel the swelling, hoping it would come to a head, break, drain, and run its course as it had with the other colts.

This was the season of the fall gathering, with cold, damp weather. Determined was away from home from before daylight until after dark. Bonita could hear his truck come and go. The children were busy at school and only came briefly to the barnyard when they were doing their evening chores. One evening, during the choring, the children popped in to see Bonita. Determined wasn't home yet and Hoss had already fed all the horses. As Bitsy came near Bonita's stall, her blue eyes widened and fright gripped her. Bonita's belabored breathing sounded more like choking. Realizing that her horse friend was in real trouble, Bitsy hurried to tell Hoss.

Everything seemed to speed up from that point in time. Dark came and Determined came. Determined, Hoss, and Bitsy came to the barn. Bitsy was carrying a big flashlight with a strong beam. Hoss had a tray from the vet supplies with disinfectant, cotton, 7 percent tincture of iodine, and long cotton swabs. Determined had command of a very sharp knife.

Bitsy stayed outside the stall but in a position with the light to focus directly upon the abscess that was causing Bonita's distress. Hoss and Determined stepped into the stall. Without consultation, they moved into their positions.

As the blade work needed to be quick and accurate, Hoss provided more security for both Determined and the colt. He didn't know if the colt would move, but he did know if he eared her, she couldn't. Determined felt the abscess; the skin was stretched tight, but in the center was a soft spot. He disinfected the area and then quickly made the cut. As he did, the puss began to pour. Hoss released the little filly gently and stood rubbing Bonita's ear and scratching her withers.

Bitsy held the flashlight without wavering. After the opening had finished draining, Determined enlarged the original opening into an X shape knowing that a small hole that might close up wouldn't be in Bonita's best interest. Even though these incisions looked terrible, they would usually heal without a noticeable scar. Hoss prepared the cotton swabs with the iodine for Determined to clean the opening. Cleaning of the cavity would be a twice-daily chore, which they would continue until the area healed from the inside out like any other wound.

Old Mama remembered how much easier it was to get her air after the ordeal of the abscess lancing and cleaning. The fellows stayed around for a while just rubbing the little filly and trying to help her in her misery. As they gathered up their things and left the barn, Hoss complimented Bitsy, "You were really good help. I'll bet you'll be a nurse someday." Bitsy didn't hesitate in her reply, "I will be a veterinarian. A horse vet."

Old Mama reflected that Bitsy had kept her vow. She was now a veterinarian. She lived in Wyoming with her rancher husband and their own children and had a busy rural practice.

Old Mama remembered that Hoss said when he was about Bitsy's age he had had a dream of being a doctor. During that time he had been a special volunteer in his hometown hospital, but his dream had drifted away when he began to drink. "The Viper" had swallowed his dream.

During the ordeal, Bonita had lost a lot of weight. For some time she didn't feel that good, but gradually she did begin to feel better. Ironically, for her young friends from the house, this was the year they caught the chicken pox: first Bossy, then Bitsy, and then Busy.

Right after the chicken pox came the mumps. One child at a time had the mumps. Even Hoss caught the mumps. Determined had to tend the traps for Hoss for almost a month. Fortunately, the weather was in a holding pattern and didn't add a blizzard to the extra workload. And, that year, spring was breaking before everyone was well and up-and-going again at the same time.

Through the fall and winter as time and weather permitted, Hoss had continued to take the Power Wagon to town to his meetings. Determined had watched his big friend grow quieter but more confident. It even seemed he was taller but that was in his carriage. One afternoon as he was scratching Bonita, Determined came into the barn. He had made the decision to turn Bonita to the colt pasture for a few months with Old Babe and the new yearlings. The other colts were going further out up to the mountain pasture. Determined would bring Bonita back in early in the summer to start breaking her. Hoss needed to tell his friend that Bonita wasn't the only one going. He knew the time had come for him to leave. He had saved most of his profits from two seasons of trapping. He was well established in his bit and spur making business. He had learned to live with The Viper "one day at a time." He hated to leave, but he needed to go.

"I will go soon, back to my home. I can help the young ones there. I can show them what I know of horses, of trapping, of the bits, and of how to lose The Viper," said Hoss quietly.

Determined had known this was coming, but he hadn't known it would hurt so badly. That was the trouble with getting too close to anyone. It always ended up hurting. He had learned that a long time ago. He should have spoken before Hoss had to be the one to bring it up. He should have released Hoss, picked a time, and taken the lead. He had known Hoss needed to leave. He should have let him go. People don't mean to hurt you, necessarily; it's just that things hurt. If you see it coming and can't fight it, the best thing to do is go with it, stay in control of things.

Determined had many facets to his personality. Bonita knew he had a dark side. He had never shown it to her, but she had observed it in a session with the leggy bay colt. Determined could be many different people but at his core was control.

Hoss and Determined's conversation was cut short by a visit from Busy. Busy needed to know if he could go into the shed and drive the old Model T Ford parked there. Some things Busy took for granted, but others were activities he usually asked permission to do. The antique Ford was something a little special. It didn't run except in Busy's imagination. In Determined's imagination, too, it would be his parade horse someday in the future. He could see himself with a load of grandkids in the Fourth of July parade.

Hoss left soon after that and summer progressed without anything eventful to mark its passing. Determined got Bonita in from pasture and began her saddle training. These sessions were usually referred to as colt breaking. Somehow this term didn't fit. Bonita tried to understand and anticipate whatever Determined wanted. If she didn't get it right, he knew she didn't understand what he wanted. He simply stopped and started over. He knew she wouldn't try to cheat him. It never even crossed his mind—nor hers.

His work with her was so quiet and calm, they were left without the usual spectators. The high school boys on the haying crew found pitching horseshoes in the evening more entertaining then watching Determined and Bonita.

Hot, late August days came and with them came the stormy afternoons. This year the rains were light or not at all, while the lightning lit up the countryside.

On one such day, Determined decided not to send the hay crew back into the field after the noon meal. He felt they needed a change of pace. He told them they could use the old gas Maytag in the shed, the one he used to wash horse blankets. This would give the fellows a chance to get their washing caught up and maybe catch an afternoon nap. The weather got hotter and cloudier. Everyone shaded up, except Busy. Busy continued to try to stir up someone or something but finally he left to entertain himself. After hanging their wash, the crew crashed. The storm came with gallons of dust and drops of rain, flashes of lightning and cracks of thunder. Then it was passed. Everyone began to come awake and take stock of their surroundings. Except for the lack of dust, things seemed as before, with one exception. No one knew where Busy was.

While the storm was present, folks in the house thought Busy was in the bunkhouse. The fellows in the bunkhouse figured he was in the house. Comparing notes, they realized no one had seen him since shortly before the storm began.

They called Dog and found him alone under the porch. They checked the barnyard and found it undisturbed. They looked in the barn, but Bonita couldn't help. He wasn't there.

Everyone regrouped in front of the bunkhouse trying to remember what he had said or did the last anyone saw of him. It came up that he had been doing a lot of talking about fishing. The river meandered through the fields and hay meadows the whole length of the ranch. The river could be gentle or at times a roaring torrent. There were shallow pools and narrow faster currents. The river was the lifeblood of the little ranch, but it was certainly not a playground for children.

The railroad also cut through the little valley, but since it was manmade, it took a more direct route than the river. The railroad was fenced to keep the livestock off the tracks.

Determined fought his fear as his mind pictured all the perils that might have befallen his little boy. He tried to keep his mind from conjecture and control the panic that was threatening to overcome him. He needed to be his most capable, collected self, to be of help to his son.

Plans were made and positions assigned to further the search for Busy. Even though there had only been a little rain, it was more than enough to wipe out most tracks in the dirt.

Just as each one was to leave to follow his part of the rescue plan, in wandered Busy. Busy was curious as to what the excitement was about. With his dirty little face and rumpled hair, he had never looked more cunning. Everyone could have hugged him, but only his dad did. He squirmed out of the embrace to explain where he had been. Earlier, when he couldn't find anyone to play with and the outside activities were threatened by rain, he had gone into the shed to look at the Model T. He really didn't know where his dad was to ask permission but he got into the T to go for a short ride. Then it got really black and stormy. He said he wasn't scared, but he crawled under an old blanket on the seat just to wait for the thunder to go away. He had only just woke up. He was sorry they were bothered. Determined grinned at the little fellow, rumpled his hair with his hand, and left shaking his head. Inside, he was still shaking. How could anyone live with the loss of a child. He was unsure about some things, but he was real sure children have guardian angels. Some children keep their angels really busy.

10

For two days after Busy's "Houdini Act," the weather stayed storm free and the crew worked hard at finishing the haying. Then the clouds began to gather and the electrical storms returned with a new energy. It seemed inevitable they would create a range fire. It was just a matter of where and when. As the danger increased the valley folks formulated a plan of defense. From Determined's spread would come the hay crew in the Power Wagon with shovels, gunnysacks, and barrels of water to wet the sacks. These were already loaded and the vehicle was kept fueled and ready. Drinking water in gallon jugs covered with gunnysacks rested in the creek, to be grabbed on the way to the Power Wagon. A box of fundamental first aid supplies and a box of dry lunch items had been packed and ready for over two weeks. A wide gauge D-6 fastened to a disc was already loaded on a lowboy near the gas pumps. The Diamond T Rio was filled and ready.

A good pair of field glasses was never far from Determined's reach as he scanned the countryside after each flash of lightning. The afternoon vigils were the most demanding, though nights could be a problem too.

One afternoon about four o'clock it happened, on a rocky outcrop on the hillside, about five miles from the home place. Because of the storm the crew was in the bunkhouse, not the fields. When the dinner bell sounded, they gathered by the vehicles for a last minute supply check and directions. The clown of the hay crew was sent back to the bunkhouse to grab his heaviest pair of boots. Directions were given and the fire-fighting crew pulled out to do battle. Determined lead the way with the truck. He would haul as near to the fire's edge as possible and then unload the D-6 and begin disking the firebreak.

The other ranchers had been alerted by the valley phone and all were rushing to take their positions. Since Determined would be busy on the firebreak, his hay crew would be working with the neighboring rancher. The kids were good help at most anything, but Determined preferred someone with gray hair direct them. They didn't lack for courage, but hadn't been around long enough for wisdom. Everyone set to his task.

Just at dark, the fire crested the mountain and began to reach long tentacles down the mountainside. It was an eerie sight. Determined thought it looked like the Devil's hand, with long clawing fingers of fire. It would be harder after dark to know where the terrain might create further hazards. He was thankful the boys with the Power Wagon were with the older rancher's crew. He was a sensible, clear thinking sort who had been on many range fires.

For several years now, one of the members of his hay crew had been a fellow they called The Vet. He was a tall, quiet worker who stayed to himself a lot. As a really young man, he had had a dream of entering the medical profession. Then a police action in the Pacific changed his life. He had been a medic during that period, but after he was discharged from the service, he had not settled on any job very long. He was a real asset to the fire-fighting crew. Determined was glad he was along, too.

During the early morning hours, the wind slowed to a whisper. The fire sputtered along seeming to be tired after its rampage of the night before. The fire crew watched and waited, putting out an occasional flare-up. Their hard work and back-fire of the previous hours looked like it might have done the job. Determined rested with his machine, after he had refueled and taken care of some maintenance. If the wind would stay calm, they had a good chance of going back home by afternoon, but in the afternoon the wind came back from a puff, to a gust, then to a gale. It came from a different direction than the previous day. It was full-blown in minutes and so was the fire. It blew up a little canyon right around the end of the carefully constructed firebreak. Determined was on his machine when he saw it coming. He was racing for his one way out. Suddenly, a wall of fire closed the escape. Courageously, Determined pushed through that wall.

The Vet and two of the boys had seen the deadly change of course. They were coming in the Power Wagon as fast as driving conditions would allow. Too late to warn Determined, they saw his machine break out. The fire swept on down the hill leaving behind a sight for which the young boys were unprepared. The sight and smell sent them reeling. This was the "Hell" the Vet knew well. He knew frontline fire burns. His training and experience took ahold of him, and he took ahold of the moment, a man machine in action. He used the first aid supplies on hand in the Power Wagon. He directed the boys where he needed them. He never questioned their ability to do as he requested. Wide-eyed and clench-jawed, in that moment they changed from boys to men.

Soon another group of the fire-fighting crew joined the medic team. The clear-thinking, older rancher assessed the damage with a heavy heart. It was a serious situation. He was thankful for the Vet's medical knowledge but it was time to head for the hospital. The Power Wagon would be the ambulance. He would drive, having the Vet and one boy ride in the back with Determined. Others were to be responsible for reaching the nearest phone to alert the hospital and the local sheriff and highway patrol. They wanted an escort when they reached the main highway. One of the other young fellows was to return to Determined's home and inform the family of the accident.

After its last violent push, the fire had hit the firebreak and was being contained.

Determined had been burned once before, a few years back, while starting a farm tractor. As he drifted in and out of consciousness, he could smell his seared flesh. He knew his neighbors were doing everything they could. When they reached the main highway, a patrol car escort was waiting. The maximum speed for the Power Wagon wasn't as much as they would have liked, but they took advantage of all they could get.

The hospital burn team was ready when they arrived, as ready as their facilities were prepared to be. Determined knew when they reached the hospital. He was thankful for relief from some of the pain.

On the rough ride to the hospital, he had fought the screaming pain. He had fought to stay somewhat conscious. He had fought to be in control of himself. Now he drifted in a space where others had total control.

The blast from the fire had fried mostly his face and neck and the left hand and arm that he had thrown up as a reflex to protect his face. The heavy cotton clothing he wore, his boots, and even his hat had been some protection.

The hospital staff did everything they could. The family came from the ranch and the waiting began. Determined's room was in Intensive Care near the nurse's station. The nurse could see inside the room and she was in and out of the room often. One of the many times she entered the room, she was shocked to find Determined was not alone. Sitting motion-less was a very large man. He looked like he belonged there, as he was in a hospital uniform. Somehow, Hoss had entered the hospital. Somehow he had found the scrub room. He had scrubbed and changed and prepared himself to be there.

When Hoss had gotten the message about his friend, he had bought gas for a neighbor to bring him to town. He had known about the fire and he knew the crew from the ranch was on the fireline. He had felt a distinct urging to be there at almost the instant of Determined's accident. Now he was here.

He went within himself, as the old one had taught him. His breathing was slow, almost as one asleep. In this trancelike condition, he reached out to connect with Determined, to connect to the life force of his fragile friend to help him through.

Since no one knew who he was or how he came to be there, no one asked him to leave. He wasn't the least in the way. When morning came and new personnel came on duty, his presence was questioned. In his predawn check, the doctor had been aware of Hoss's support of his patient. The doctor knew medicine well and he knew not all healing was from medicine. The doctor gave orders to allow Hoss to stay. He stayed. Normally, Hoss was a hearty eater who liked his morning coffee, but in his trancelike state he didn't even smell the fresh coffee down the hall.

Through the morning Determined seemed to be drifting in and out. Hoss was aware of his torment. He used all his strength to stay connected and send only strength to his fallen friend. He willed Determined to feel connected, so he could share with him his strength, his confidence and caring. Near noon the doctor and a team entered the room. Hoss took the opportunity to leave for a few minutes. When he returned, Determined seemed to be less agitated. Perhaps he was more sedated.

The day wore into night. Hospital staff came and went. Hoss sat quietly in the corner of the room. After midnight, Hoss sensed something different about Determined. He watched closely as the nurses came and went. He watched as they filled out their charts. The something different did not show on the charts, but Hoss didn't like what he felt. He watched more intently than before.

Then it happened. Determined felt a great release from the horrible pain. A bright glow just outside the window moved closer inside the room. It was welcomed. Then suddenly a huge shape moved between him and the light, and a deep voice demanded him not to go. The pain came back. The nurses came and went. The doctor came and went. Determined and Hoss stayed in the room. Hoss hadn't seen the light Determined had seen, but he had known it was there. At daybreak, the doctor told the family the crisis had passed. Hoss waited to be sure, but in midmorning he made arrangements to go to the little cow outfit. That was where his friend needed him now.

11

The fall after the terrible range fire, Bonita found herself again living in the little stall and run on the end of the barn. The last two falls she had been there so she could receive extra care. This year was different. It seemed she was there to give care. Hoss came in the evenings to scratch Bonita and to share his concerns for their mutual friend. Determined's burns were healing better than the doctor had hoped; in time, they would leave only scars. The obvious outside injures were responding to treatment, but his eyes held a deep, haunting pain. Hoss worried about that.

The children, too, came to the barn. They came with a little extra handful of hay, an apple or a palm of grain. In their need to be cared for, they cared for Bonita and shared their fears. When the time came for Determined to re-enter his outside world, Bonita was there waiting. When he came through the barn door, he stood as if unsure. Bonita pushed against her stall door, leaned out over the top and began to talk to him in low, whinnying sounds. He grinned and came to greet her, same walk, same talk, she remembered from the hail storm her first summer. Oh! She was so pleased to be with him again. When he took her head between his two gloved hands, she sent him all the strength and healing she could will. Feeling him there with her, she knew he would get well.

After that, he came to the barn quite often. He began to talk of what the two of them would do come spring. He made plans for her three-year-old year and for the year she would be a four-year-old. All their preparation would take them to compete in the Snaffle Bit class at the county fair in the fall of 1959.

That winter brought enough moisture to lift the fear of drought. It seemed to come quite early in predictable storm patterns. Every few days a little more snow came in manageable measure. Often, it fell softly and piled up on the fence posts. It was a gentle, quiet winter.

At the little cow ranch they were not snowed in nor snowed out all winter. The children never missed a day of school from illness or bad weather. All the winter's supplies were in early. The wood shed and fuel tanks, the pantry and cellar were all filled. Every conceivable spare part for machinery or horse equipment was stored in the shop. Their preparedness was so complete their needs were met early and they had no awareness of wants. The events of the previous season had stressed and stretched them all. They welcomed this season's days of quiet sameness. They remembered it long after as their Winter of Peace. Everyone had time, time for everything! Determined had time to get well, time to heal and time to whittle some little carvings of wood. He had time to play the harmonica for the children and time to visit with Hoss and Bonita. Hoss had time to feed the cattle, to make some snowshoes, and to tend his traps. Hoss had time to work on bit orders. In and of itself, the gift of time is the greatest healer of all.

Winter left as gently and quietly as it had come. One day at a time it melted and slipped away into spring. Spring grew into summer with new calves, green grass, and plenty of water for irrigation. Hoss stayed on and, with the help of high school boys on weekends, was able to keep ahead of the ranch's needs.

Determined helped the kids and Hoss start a few colts. Determined had lots of time to spend riding Bonita and his older horses, as he left the new colts for Hoss. Since Determined had missed the fair the fall before, he was anxious to go with several horses exceptionally ready. Bonita would be hauled in to the fair also and used in the cow working to turn back or do whatever Determined felt would help prepare her for her debut event the following year.

That summer's hay crop was heavy. It was cut, baled, and stacked with few storms and fewer machinery breakdowns. Hoss set the pace. He was a natural leader. He didn't wear a watch but seemed to have an internal clock, which allowed him to always be a little early. His sense of time allowed him to be ahead of the need and to head off many a potential problem. The young fellows of the hay crew first observed his gift as "luck." Before the season was finished, they referred to it differently. They began to observe him more closely. They would try to see what he saw, feel what he felt, and think as he thought. It was a wonderful growing season. Determined enjoyed watching his big friend work with the younger boys, two on the crew had come over from Hoss's cousin's household. They were some boys Hoss had begun to work with the summer before in his home area.

Then it was county fair time again. Old Mama shifted her weight. How well she remembered her first trip to town. The first day at the fair grounds was pretty quiet, compared with what happened the next few days. There were lots of young people, young people with serious 4-H projects and other young people with water balloons. They seemed to be always chasing someone or something. It was pretty exciting to see a twelve hundred-pound steer go by, dragging a 120-pound 4-Her. Usually, some adult would be able to intervene just before things got really out of control. Mostly, it didn't bother Bonita; she was fairly used to a barnyard full of excitement.

When the race horses began to arrive, that was quite a different matter. If Bonita had not had full confidence in Determined, no telling what would have happened the first time they came tearing around the track. She just couldn't imagine what terrible monster was pursuing them, to cause such a full out run for their lives!

There were quiet times around the stalls between events and classes. Eager and his family were there from out-of-state. Other ranchers were in town with their stock horse entries. This was an opportunity to exchange ideas. For the most part, the talk was about horses. They talked pedigrees and merits of each bloodline. They didn't always agree. They talked about saddles and types of gear. There were some differences of opinion. They talked about methods of starting horses. There was a wide variety of ideas about that, but they all agreed about the importance of the horse in their lives and liveli-hood.

One evening, chore time brought a discussion about "women's work." One very young, cocky, would-be-Buckaroo seated on a bale of hay commented on the obvious ease of "women's work."

That was when Bonita first became really aware of the big rancher who owned the dark gelding. He questioned the cocky, young fellow to see where his opinion came from. It turned out the young man had very little firsthand knowledge of the subject he claimed to be so knowledgeable about. Bonita had noticed earlier the dark gelding's owner seemed to hold quite a bit of respect among the other exhibitors. When they had discussed bloodlines and pedigrees, he could recite the complete book. When the talk was saddles and gear, he had a fair showing to share. The horses he continually brought to exhibit at the fair spoke for his colt-starting meth-ods. Until now, no one had heard what he thought about "women's work."

Then he said, "When I was a young fellow, about as wise as you are now, I once had an opportunity to make some easy money doing 'women's work.' The folks who lived down the road a bit needed to be out of the area for three or four days. They had four children and a few animals to care for, and they offered to pay me what I usually made day working in the hay. Well, I knew their kids and they were well mannered and fun to be around. They always seemed to go about the place taking care of their chores with not much fuss and they were all old enough to watch after themselves pretty well. I knew I had it made. Their folks left on Friday, mid-morning and they were back before chore time Monday evening. Seems that was the longest, most difficult weekend, I every spent....

"The mother of the kids had all the washing done up, and the house was really clean. She had baked ahead three pies, including my very favorite apple. She had baked a chocolate fudge-covered, layered cake and a yellow, flat cake with lemon frosting. The cookie jar was full of cookies. She had left a pot roast cooked with vegetables, a big pan of spaghetti, a pot of brown beans, and some stew. She left a detailed list of how I was to warm up every meal. There was more than enough food and suggestions and directions for a hay crew for a week.

"Just like I thought, the kids were no bother. They were well and healthy, in their own space, and knew the routine. The oldest boy milked the cow and fed the pigs. The older girl fed the chickens and gathered the eggs and the little girl followed along. The youngest boy fed the dogs. Meal time, and bedtime too, they had their routine. The oldest girl helped put things on the table. They were pretty good eaters. All but the smallest took their plates to the sink after the meal. The oldest girl took care of her sister's plate and helped clear the table. They took turns helping with the dishes. In the bedtime routine, the big sister took care of the little one, from bathing to bedtime story and night prayers. The boys managed on their own. There was a list posted in the bathroom to check about washing and brushing teeth and such. Posted around that house were several lists, enough to take up two dozen areas of concern. But for the other ten dozen situations, there was nothing that could be prepared.

"Friday, I did pretty well. It seemed there was some momentum going. There were only minor problems; some I created for myself, just warming up the meals. Saturday, about the first thing, the mailman ran over the cat. I swear, one car and one cat in one hundred square miles more or less. I really don't know how I would have managed if I had needed to be the vet. Being the gravedigger, undertaker, and preacher and carving the marker took all morning.

"I scorched the spaghetti reheating it for the noon meal. It tasted awful, but the kids weren't hungry anyway. I didn't have the kitchen cleaned up yet when the boys got into a fight. I got out there to straighten things out, which took some doing. The oldest girl was yelling about, 'Goin' to tell Momma.' The little girl was crying again. She had been crying off and on ever since the cat died. She had so many concerns and questions about the dead cat, I was wishin' the cat had never been born.

"Since the kids hadn't eaten much at noon, they were hungry again before two. I lost control with the first peanut butter and jelly sandwich. They were in and out of the kitchen and pantry till dark. Somewhere in between, I fixed the supper. They all dirtied their plates, so I had the same amount of dishes, but nobody ate. I had loaded up on chocolate cake and I wasn't very hungry either.

"Finally, they were in bed asleep. I spent the next three hours doing the strung out dishes and trying to put things in order. Seemed it was easier to mop the whole kitchen and pantry then to wipe up spills and spots. I went to sleep wishing for Monday. The kids didn't seem to rest well that night. After losing their cat, then the feeding frenzy, trying to stuff the hurt away, it was near morning when they stopped tossing, turning, and talking in their sleep.

"The next morning I was real quiet, as long as I could be. I didn't care if the chores were late. I wanted them to sleep as long as they would. I was determined that day to hold my own, keeping the meals on time and the house clean, but I hadn't factored in the rainstorm and a rainbow, a big splinter under a tiny fingernail, a spilled and broken pitcher of milk, and a half-grown chicken that didn't cross the pig pen quick enough. All these things take attention and explaining.

"By evening the little one was crying for her Mama, and I was about to!

"After they were safe in bed and I had cleaned the whole place up as best I could, I crashed on the sofa. I sat there looking around at 'women's work.' I was exhausted and I hadn't really cooked or baked. I hadn't washed and ironed. I hadn't made curtains or doilies, framed pictures, or made rugs. I got tireder thinking about it.

"I got up and went to check on the children. They were all sleeping pretty well. I got sort of a lump in my throat. I remember thinking how glad I was they had a mother. Every since then, I have been pretty much in awe of the ones who can do 'women's work' so well."

When the story was finished, the young fellow left the bale of hay. He didn't have anything else to say. Talk turned back to horses.

Bonita watched the storyteller with interest. He sure was a dependable one. He was so helpful and friendly with all the other riders. Bonita began to think of him as the Dependable One.

Being at the fair grounds was an exciting time for Bonita. Since Determined had several other horses to ride, she spent quite a lot of time in her stall, watching all the activity in the barn area.

Hoss had stayed on the ranch to keep things cared for, but he came to town sometime everyday to watch the classes. He was most interested in the classes where Determined was competing. Determined had the flashy sorrel in the Snaffle Bit class. He was such a good looking colt. Determined called him Flashy Soxs. He was flashy to look at, but he really didn't have the flashy moves Determined loved in a horse. His dam was a dark sorrel, with a snip and strip and only a little white on the coronary bands of both hind feet. She wasn't very colorful, but she was sweet natured and passed it to her offspring, most of which had more color than she. Determined liked her colts because they fit so many buyers' needs. Some of the bloodlines he had been breeding had a lot more action, but they needed more riding it seemed. He usually never found a buyer for them until they matured and were well along in the bridle. Sorrel Mama's colts were saleable from the time they hit the ground. Anybody could love them.

The day Determined competed on Flashy Soxs, Bonita was there waiting. Hoss had come from the ranch in time to help Determined saddle and warm up. Determined had ridden Bonita to the arena and in among the other horses for a while. Hoss was on the sorrel. Hoss stayed with Bonita by the outgate while the class was showing. Bonita felt the blood rush through her veins when Determined took the single cow down the fence. How she wished she were under Flashy Soxs' skin for a little more speed and a harder turn back.

Determined and Flashy carried a second place ribbon back to the barn area. There was a big revolving trophy in the class. A rider had to win it three times to retire the trophy. There was always next year. At this fair, Blue Roan did the ranch proud, winning two different bridle classes and Pard won the Two-Rein class even though the competition was tight.

Most of the other happenings were routine, pretty much what would be expected at the county fair. The one rider who had everyone's attention was a lanky fellow on a chestnut gelding. He won the Open Bridle class. What had everyone talking was not his win but his unusual antics when he worked his single cow on the fence. He did a phony near fall-off maneuver that should have caused him whiplash. It was quite a sight.

Back in the barn space, Bonita liked to watch the fellows

come and go and visit. She noticed early how Hoss's presence affected the group. Children were instinctively drawn to him. Animals were especially comfortable with him. Strangely though, not all the tall people were comfortable with him.

Old Mama shifted her weight. She stretched her standing leg and thought about that. Humankind were a puzzle. They seemed to begin life pretty accepting. By instinct, they seemed to feel their kinship with one another. Somewhere along the way, they made a different turn. A lot of folks didn't come back for a long time or ever. That seemed like a terrible waste.

The evening the fair was over, everything was loaded to return to the ranch. Eager and his family came to the ranch, too. They were going to help with all the unloading, all the extra work of returning from the fair. Determined and Eager hadn't had much chance to visit and they welcomed this time. Eager had made a move or so since being in his new state. He wasn't content about things, but he did feel he was making some progress with his horses. He was showing a little and getting to meet quite a number of people.

Eager and his family left early the next morning. Determined's outfit began the fall routine. There was a lot to do. The school kids had a pretty, new teacher. She did things a bit differently. It was easier for Bitsy to accept change than it was for Bossy. Busy was new enough at everything that things were fine with him.

That particular year, winter came before Halloween and stayed until after Easter. Bonita stayed in the barn stall again. Determined told Hoss he thought he would just keep her close. He would likely use her whenever he needed to do anything on horseback. It would be real handy to have her in the barn. Hoss agreed, even though he suspected a deeper reason. Having her in the barn was a little extra work, but they had all gotten used to that routine.

They had to feed hay all that winter and had lots of fierce

weather to contend with. When spring finally came, it would be welcomed.

Hoss had a good season trapping on the river. During the long evenings, he had created new designs in his silver work. Determined had "thinking time" that winter and one evening he followed Hoss to the shop. Hoss stayed busy working the silver and waited.

Pretty soon, Determined said, "I've been pushing the pencil a lot this winter. There is a fellow up the valley who will contract my haying; I figure I'll try that. The big snow pack should give us plenty of water so I can handle the irrigating." He hesitated. Hoss waited. "There is a new pickup in the budget. That old Power Wagon isn't even on the books. Most everything you got would fit into the Power Wagon." Hoss looked deep into his friend's eyes. Determined returned the look and continued, "I'll help you pack and you can go home whenever you are ready." Hoss nodded. He continued to work the silver. The talk moved to the merits of various bits.

It was less than a week until Hoss was gone. When the subject had come up, there was a bit of a lull in the ranch work. Everyone was well, busy and happy. It seemed the door was open for him to leave. Hoss had a good talk with Bitsy; they sat on a hay bale near Bonita's stall, as he told her how important this little family was to him. He assured her he wouldn't be that far away. He was really only four or so hours driving time and one heartbeat away. He told her he was a fire, flood, blizzard, "be there" kind of guy. Even when she grew up if she moved further away, the distance would only be one heartbeat.

She grinned and said, "You know I'll test you!" She could handle his leaving.

The talk with Busy went rather well. He was most interested in when he could go visit Hoss for a weekend or a week.

Bossy wouldn't talk about Hoss leaving. She wouldn't talk to Hoss. She couldn't say "good-bye."

Old Momma's Story

Determined talked nonstop all the time he helped Hoss pack and load the Power Wagon. He told funny stories and kidded about Hoss's future being full of a wife and ten kids. When the Power Wagon was loaded, he handed Hoss the title for the vehicle, shook hands, and stepped back. Hoss drove away.

12

In her mind's eye, Old Mama saw again the robins bathing in the snow thaw puddles; they were a welcome sight. Finally, spring was coming. It came all right, too fast. As the frost left the ground and the snow melted, everything became a bog. It was too soon for grass and the ground became a difficult, muddy mess to try to feed and care for the stock.

Then the heavy mountain snowpack let loose and began its descent towards lower ground. The river began to rise quickly.

Before breakfast on the third morning of the thaw, the phone rang. The neighbor at the head of the valley was so excited he could hardly talk. His message was, "It's coming!"— a wall of water like he'd never seen before in his thirty-two years in the valley.

Determined left the house walking fast. He put his rough-out saddle on Bonita and jogged towards the lower meadow. He wasn't concerned for the home and outbuildings. They were on high enough ground, but he had a little bunch of late calving heifers down in a low meadow. If the river jumped the bank and cut across the field, they would be stranded on an island or swept away. He was thankful for the time he had spent on Bonita; she now had some seasoning. He was thankful Dog was part of the team; Dog was a good hand. Determined was thankful for the trace of frost in the ground. It made for a little better footing. Too bad it hadn't frozen up above, instead of raining.

When Determined, Bonita, and Dog reached the lower field,

the gathering went real well, thanks to Dog. There weren't any calves yet and Determined was thinking he'd just drive them to the little hillside field above the house. They would be well out of the path of the possible flood. When he got off to close the gate, Dog disappeared. Before he had fastened the gate, Dog reappeared, hustling a stray they had missed. She had been calving in a low spot in the willows. Being young and confused, she was moving to catchup with the others. Dog was making sure she did. The calf was left behind.

Determined knew the calf was a preemie, probably be puny—likely die anyway—wouldn't be worth a dollar bill. He ought to leave it. These were the thoughts rolling through his head as he hurried back to rescue the calf.

Bonita was getting a little leg-weary as the ground was now soft, but she stayed with Determined all the way. She stood like a veteran when he gathered up the calf and mounted. It was cold but Determined broke out in a cold sweat as he realized what he had feared had happened: The river had jumped its bank. It was on a raging shortcut between them and the house field. Dog and the heifers were still moving toward higher ground, quite safe.

Determined never slackened nor quickened their pace. He knew every inch of that meadow. He had hayed it and irrigated it, both in the daylight and the dark. He headed down along the water where he knew there was a levee used to hold the water during irrigating. This narrow, submerged ridge could give them just the edge they needed.

Old Mama shivered remembering that rushing water. They moved, step ahead of step, as the water beat against her legs. Step and step again as the water whirled and churned and so did her insides. She wanted to fling herself forward but she went step-by-step, and then stepped into shallow water, then onto the boggy ground. They continued their steady walk to the barn. Determined put the preemie calf in a pile of hay. Bitsy had seen them coming and ran to the barn to meet them. Bonita's body was quivering inside and out. Determined took the saddle off and began to rub her with some burlap grain sacks. While he rubbed, he talked about how wonderful she was. Bitsy ran to the house for old towels. She took over caring for Bonita and insisted her Dad take care of himself.

Before Determined could return to the barn, Bitsy was in the kitchen warming up a little "first milk" from the freezer. This wasn't the first little orphan calf she had mothered. It turned out Dollar Bill was a heifer, which made her worth even less. Bitsy didn't care about that sort of math. Bitsy would give the little one every chance to live—and live she did.

From the flood until fall, the ranch seemed to be under siege. One thing after another came up to test them. Finally, it was county fair time again. Ready or not, it was that time of year. Eager usually tried to have time off about then. He and his family liked to visit in the area during the fair because everyone from miles around was there.

He came a day early, as he had in past years, to help Determined with the preparation for hauling to the fair. This year Determined had at least one horse for every class. The Blue Roan and Pard were in the Bridle class. Rawhide was in the Two Rein class. Flashy Soxs was in the Hackamore and two entries were in the Snaffle Bit class; one of the colts was a younger brother to Flashy Soxs. He was really kind, not as colorful as Flashy, but with plenty of class. He had a snip and a strip on his face and two low stockings behind. The other one was Bonita.

This year was to be Bonita's big chance. She had seen that class the year before. She had seen the trophy up close. The revolving trophy would not be retired until someone won it three times. There were three names now on it, twice each. One of the names was Determined's.

Old Mama felt again the excitement of that trip to town, loaded in the stock truck with the other performance horses. This time she was to have a role to play in the events.

When they were stabled at the fairgrounds, she was pleased to discover she was in the same stall she had occupied the season before. On either side of her were Determined's horses. Just across in the facing stalls, the other three were stabled. She was neighbor to Blue Roan and Flashy Soxs. Across from her were Pard, Rawhide and the sorrel Snaffle Bit colt. He had been named Blanco Strip.

Dependable was in town with a couple entries. He had a Hackamore horse and one in the Bridle. Bonita remembered him and his dark gelding. More than that she remembered his story about "woman's work." There were quite a few other ranchers with their horses. She remembered seeing them last year but she had not gotten to know them.

It seemed to Bonita there was always a cluster of riders around or near Dependable. He was a little older than most of them and it appeared they all respected his opinion. When the conversation turned to the various philosophies and methods of horse training, Dependable had the floor. They all wanted to hear what he had to say.

He chuckled when he said, "It has always fascinated me when I hear a rider say, 'He has never had a lesson in his life—he is completely self-taught.'" He continued, "Granted, in my life experiences I have not seen everything. However, I have yet to see a small child with a great amount of knowledge about horses. This leaves me believing that everyone learns somewhere from someone. I am grateful for every horseman whoever tried to pass his expertise on to me. My problem is when I try to give credit to them, the listener often interprets me saying I do things *like* the horseman who introduced me to that thought or action. Since no two riders or two horses are alike, it seems obvious to me that I will not be doing things *like* some other horseman, but you can bet I'll be doing my very best and hoping to get better." With his last remark, Dependable moved off to care for his horses.

Down at the end of the row of stalls was a fast walking

fellow who didn't talk a lot. He had a well-made entry for the Open Bridle class and a black and white gelding for the Snaffle Bit class. This fellow already had his name twice on the Snaffle Bit revolving trophy. It looked like he was planning to take that trophy home. His Open Bridle entry was intimidating competition by just being there. Leading him out of the stall, he looked like he was heading towards a Halter Class trophy. His Texas sire had been a leading sire of performance and halter horses for years. He and Paint would be hard to beat. Bonita had heard the black and white gelding didn't have papers, but he surely had breeding.

Determined was pretty impressed with the fellow's bridle horse. He and Eager were discussing that entry when Dependable came to feed his horses. Dependable knew the history and pedigree of both the dam and sire. He could sure be depended upon to know his horse facts.

The first class to perform in the morning would be the Snaffle Bit class. There were a lot of entries, so there would be an elimination round. Since Determined had two entries for the class, Eager would be there early to help.

At first light the next day, most of the riders were in the barn area. Bonita was not surprised to see Hoss. He was the first person in the stall area that morning, she was glad to see him and get her special scratching. She knew he would be there after the competition and that nothing would change between them regardless of the outcome. Hoss liked to come to the fair and watch the classes. He especially liked the classes where Determined had an entry. Most of Determined's horses were Hoss's friends. He was interested in their progress. He knew it was part of the survival of the little ranch to produce good performance horses. Fair time was an opportunity for potential buyers, and Hoss knew well Determined's struggle to keep financially afloat. Many a time he had seen the pressure bear down on Determined. He had seen Determined bear down on his entries. On more than one occasion he had seen

Determined ask for more and more again—and get it. As he scratched Bonita, he wondered how it would go today. When the fast walking fellow led Paint out, Hoss let out a long breath. It was easy to see he bested Bonita in every muscle. Paint was taller, longer, and stronger in every way. He and his rider were well prepared for the competition. Hoss continued to scratch Bonita.

Soon Determined and Eager were there and the pace picked up. Without obvious hassle, lots of things were accomplished. Determined and Eager were a good team. Hoss had an easy way of speeding things along without seeming to do much.

Determined rode Bonita to the warm-up arena. Eager rode Blanco Strip. The warm-up area wasn't crowded yet. Everyone was pretty relaxed, or so it seemed.

Old Mama thought back on all her years of competition. The first was the most exciting. She had rather liked being among the other horses and riders.

Everyone, horses and riders alike, were decked out in what Determined referred to as "their company best." The saddle Determined used most on the ranch had a little basket stamp, but for show he rode a rose-carved J. M. Capriola. A lot of work had gone into that saddle and more than one paycheck, back when Determined buckarooed for hire. The double Navajo beneath the saddle was hand woven and dyed with natural dyes. Bonita felt she really lived up to her name. She knew they made a pretty picture circling the arena.

Old Mama had been entered in many events since then, some she could roughly remember, but firsts are forever. She wondered what Golden Son was experiencing. His first competition was a major event in the horse world and not much like a small town county fair.

After Determined rode Bonita to warm up, he switched his show saddle to Blanco Strip. Hoss stayed with Bonita. He talked to her and scratched her favorite scratch spots. They were in an ideal place outside the arena to watch the competition being judged. Since Determined had two entries, he and Blanco Strip were second to perform. Bonita performed next to last in the class.

Looking back, she realized how much Hoss had steadied and comforted her. His being there had kept her from fretting. Her first time showing had been quite easy. She didn't remember all the details of the elimination class, but she remembered going back to the barn area and how pleased Determined was to hear the announcer include both Bonita's and Blanco Strip's entry numbers for the finals in the afternoon. It was Determined's policy to do no more than necessary to make the morning cut. A spectator seeing him for the first time would hardly notice his work.

Determined never ate anything when the rest of the fellows went for grub. When the final class was called, he was ready. He knew the judge, the footing in the arena, the cattle, the competition, and the crowd. He knew his horse. He knew how to handle them all.

Eager and Hoss watched him warm up Blanco Strip for the finals. They knew he wanted to place at least a third on Blanco Strip to keep him looking solid, to cinch a sale he was working towards. That left little Bonita to beat out Paint for the trophy. They talked in low voices about the chances. Paint had gone full out in the morning event to impress the judge and the crowd. He did both. But, morning points didn't carry to the finals. That was good, as Determined had saved all he could on both his entries. Bonita would need all she had: strength, speed, and alertness. They worried that that wouldn't be enough.

As they stood outside the arena watching the finalists, they finally voiced aloud their fears. As long time friends of Determined, they knew him well. They knew he came to take home the trophy. They knew when the stakes were high enough; he would demand much of his mount. They had seen him under pressure many times. They knew first hand how much pressure he could put on a horse, but Bonita was different. Bonita had been different ever since he led her home beside the Blue Roan. He was connected to her in a way he had never seemed to be with any other horse. Determined and Bonita were so connected Eager wondered aloud how that connection would affect the outcome.

After the reining pattern, Paint and Bonita were tied in points. What Paint had used up in the eliminations appeared to leave him a little less sharp. The afternoon temperature was warming up, and Paint was not accustomed to the altitude. Determined was careful in the herd work. He knew the contest would be won, or lost, with the single cow down the fence. After the herd work, Bonita was one point ahead.

There was a tense quiet while the herd was put away and the judge took a new position on the fence. The man on Paint took a fresh chew and rode away from the other entries gathered near the gate. Determined sat quietly on Blanco Strip and waited. Hoss began to rub and scratch Bonita. Eager visited with the gate man.

Even though there were more than two entries, the real contest had narrowed down to just Paint and Bonita. When Paint's number was called, his owner spit out his chew and entered the gate. He rode forward and tugged on the brim of his Stetson. He was ready. If there is such a thing as an ideal steer for fence work competition, Paint drew one. He held it on the end, while it tested him just enough. He was looking good. When he let it down the fence, the animal hugged the fence and made a good hard escape run. Paint caught and controlled it in both directions, brought it off the fence, and circled it both ways. He gave the judge the work he had described in the instructions. Paint's owner was pleased. The crowd was pleased. While the judge was writing, he looked pleased.

Not many folks watching were concentrating on the next

horse to show; few remembered anything about that work. But everyone there remembered Bonita's first fence work competition.

Old Mama felt young blood running through her veins as she remembered with clarity every second of that ride.

As they moved into the arena to position for the cow, Determined's body was alive and alert, but there was a controlled quietness about him. Eager's pulse quickened. Hoss let out a long breath. Bonita sensed what Hoss and Eager were concerned about. It was true. Determined would take whatever the little filly wanted to give. He would ask for nothing more. She felt him give her unconditional, total acceptance. What they shared was a dimension far above contests and crowds. They moved together and he signaled for their cow. The animal burst through the gate head high and wild-eyed. Being careful and playing it cool, they looked as good as Paint and his owner had, holding and controlling their animal on the end. When that heifer blew snot and broke down the fence, everybody knew she was headed far out. She would go through, over, or under any obstacle in her path. For a split second, Bonita felt unsure as they faded left to intercept that heifer. Then from deep within came a force that propelled her forward. She dug in hard in a burst of speed. She came in fast and blocked that heifer nose to nose. There was so much dust the spectators thought they were witnessing a wreck. For a second Determined was loosened in his seat. The crowd was on the edge of theirs. Determined was with Bonita when she overtook and blocked her challenger the second time. After being stopped so completely twice, the heifer was no longer a challenge. Completing the circle work was somewhat routine to Bonita, but the crowd was on its feet cheering.

After the heifer was taken from the arena, Determined dismounted to retrieve his hat. That was something of a first, too; no one could remember him ever loosing his headgear, his seat, or his confidence. He led the little filly out and kept walking past the other riders. He needed space and time. His little filly was breathing hard and needed to be cooled out and cared for. The contest was over. Actually, it was over just before the fence work began. The oneness they had shared defied description. He was shaken to the core. This man of control had shared with another creature more than he ever had before and it frightened him.

The scores were tallied. The score sheets were handed to the announcer. The class was called in front of the grandstand for the presentation. But to Determined the awards presentation was something of an anticlimax. Eager rode Blanco Strip and received his third place award for Determined. Paint was second.

Determined and Bonita carried out the trophy.

13

Back in the barn area, after the Snaffle Bit class finals, there was a lot of excitement around Bonita's stall. Hoss and Eager were there, of course, and Dependable. Others came by to congratulate Determined and Bonita.

One of the first ones to come was a fellow Bonita had seen the year before, and sometimes visiting at the home ranch. He was of a similar size and build as Determined. He was of the same family. Their outside appearance was a lot alike but inside they were quite different. This fellow didn't seem as driven as Determined. He could recognize the power plays, all the one-upsman stuff, and not take a role. He was always geared to do his personal best but didn't have a problem with perfect. He was more cowman than cowboy, a pretty capable fellow.

After the main group of well-wishers had drifted away, Determined had gone to have coffee with Blanco Strip's potential buyer. The Capable One and Eager shared a baled straw seat and a visit.

Capable was making a decision. His circumstances had created a situation where he needed to make choices. He had a good position as a cowboss on a large spread. He liked the job. The owners liked him. The crew appreciated and liked him. He could work alone or with a crew. He never asked anyone to do anything he couldn't do. This gave the fellows of the crew confidence.

Actually, he had already mentally made his choice and he needed now to just follow through. He especially liked the open range and the life far from town, but life at the end of the dirt road didn't fit the needs of his growing children. He had made a choice some years back to marry and have a family; he was committed to being a family man. His first child was of school age and he knew these were important developmental years for children. Soon there would be Scouts and 4-H, school band and sports.

As they sat visiting, they saw a fellow they both knew. He was coming toward them with a gal they didn't know "hanging all over him." They knew it wasn't his wife. When the fellow saw them, he changed directions and cut through between the stalls.

Capable observed his retreat. He took a straw from the bale and chewed on it before he spoke, "As time goes on and I've seen this so much, I've come to the conclusion, my Gramps was right: 'Liars lie and cheaters cheat.' It has less to do with what their women folks do, or don't do, and more to do with the men of the family tree. It's a 'Hell of a Heritage.'"

Nearly twenty years later, strictly by coincidence, Old Mama saw the Cheater Man again. He had come by Missy's to look at some foals she had for sale. They were consigned to her by a friend. Capable came to look at the same foals and their talk led to their families. Capable inquired about the fellow's son and daughter. He knew the man was proud of his children and especially his pretty little girl. She had always meant so much to him and he had so protected her.

Cheater said they were both grown and married. His son was having marriage problems. He was having a hard time settling down and being true to his wife, but he couldn't really blame him; his son's wife had let herself go since the children—"You know how it goes," he added. His voice changed when he mentioned his daughter, his darling, his precious. She was everything a gal could be—slender and beautiful, talented and charming, a good mother and a great housekeeper and cook. She had married an S.O.B. who cheated on her. It was breaking her heart and his, too. She sure hadn't done anything to deserve this.

Capable knew the daughter and he quite agreed. She hadn't done anything to deserve this "Hell of a Heritage."

After Cheater's interruption, the conversation turned back to work conditions in Eager's area, opportunities and attitudes around the horse part of the cattle industry. Eager confirmed what Capable had heard rumored, horse competitions were changing from the days of ranch-type horses, ridden by folks off the ranch. A new type was becoming prominent. The new breed was classed as "horse trainers." They were paid to produce winners. They would do whatever it took to get results. Sometimes force and fear became the quickest way.

Just recently Eager had visited a well-established trainer. The paraphernalia in the tack room had left him aghast. There were things he had never seen before. There were gag-bits, double twisted wire snaffles, be-nice halters, homemade quick stops, bosals made of bicycle chains and other things that made him question the trainer's methods and motives.

After the talk about the trainer's tack room, the conversation turned to Eager's new job. He was excited about the job. He had moved several times in the last few years, but he felt this job was going to work for him. He was really honestly eager to please this boss. As a kid at home he had never felt like he was able to please his father. It seemed he would go faster and harder, but no matter the stretch it always seemed out of reach.

Capable listened and was concerned for this Eager fellow. Eager mentioned the irrigator on the ranch had been ill. He had been doing his job. Before Capable left the straw seat, he gave Eager some advice, "If you've been hired to cowboy, don't get off your horse."

He went on to explain, "It's not because you're too good to do it. It's a matter of mathematics. If the ranch needed one fellow to look after the cattle, one for the water, and one person to do chores and maintenance, they are all needed. They lose the irrigator and you do the job. The chore man quits and you take over that work, too. Pretty soon you are working three times as hard and doing a poor job on all three counts. You'll please no one, get frustrated and quit, or get fired. There are usually hard feelings either way." Eager listened, but he didn't really hear. He was so enthusiastic to please his boss—somewhere, some way, some day, there would be a father figure he could please.

Determined came back to feed his horses and everyone left for the night. The rest of the fair sped by swiftly. Determined's other horses performed and placed about as he had figured they would.

Thinking back, Old Mama realized the biggest upset about the fair that year had happened in the Snaffle Bit class. No one had predicted the hometown horse would outpoint the competition. She relived her trophy moment with a warm glow.

The other new happening was the "fast walking" man's Texas bred horse; he was a dandy. All the fellow competitors were unmistakably taken with the form of that mount. Old Mama could not remember that any one was surprised or disappointed when he won the Open Bridle class.

Determined was so impressed with Fast Walker's horse, he had spent extra time getting better acquainted with his owner. He had to know if there were more horses like him at the fellow's home ranch. Determined was excited by what he found. He felt he had hit the jackpot when Fast Walker told him he owned a young stallion that was a full brother to the winner of the Open Bridle class. He was a colt that had gotten injured as a yearling. The injury prevented him from competition but wouldn't affect his performance as a sire. Fast Walker was looking for a few good mares to breed in the coming season, as he really wanted to prove his stud. He did not plan to breed many outside mares. He would only breed to the best.

By the end of the fair, Determined had formulated a plan. He had figured out how he could make the plan work. He and the stud's owner worked it all out and shook on it. It was a done deal. In the early spring, Bonita would leave her home. She would go to this fellow's stud farm. Bonita would produce a new stud for the future of Determined's ranch. If this Texas bloodline was the future in stock horses, he was determined to be part of the future.

People used to say of Determined, "He could sell anything." By the end of the fair, he had quite convinced the stud's owner of the desirability of breeding Bonita to his stud. The fact that she had beaten his Paint didn't hurt the decision in Bonita's favor.

The stud farm was in the southern part of the state, where there was very little winter. Determined planned to keep Bonita in the stall again this winter. This would give him the opportunity to really concentrate on her health and welfare. He could blanket her. Since he had just recently put electricity in her part of the barn, he might even use lights to aide her in having an early heat season. As usual, with Determined, he had a plan down to the smallest detail. That was how his mind worked. His father had always told him, "If you can duplicate it in your mind—down to the smallest detail—it's yours, nine-tenths of the job is done." Determined did not know how accurate the percentage was, but he did know the power of a well-pictured plan.

He knew too, he couldn't just determine the sex of Bonita's coming foal by dreaming of a new stud—*but he could dream*!

Less than a year and half later when the foal came, he was a miniature miracle, with all the muscles in the right places, a good mind in the middle and deep within, the heart and will of his mother.

Old Mama flicked a fall fly and dreamed about the past. How simple and sheltered her life was during her early years at Determined's spread. She had no thought of how her life would change because of events at that year's fair. Before Determined hauled his horses home from the fair, he had figured out many changes and was well into making them happen.

During the early morning feeding on the last fair day, Determined took the opportunity to discuss his plans with Eager. He wanted Eager's help to find the perfect future home for Bonita. He had been thinking. He really wanted to breed his special filly. He wanted her bloodline in his future stock horses. After all these seasons of being the special horse for the household, he couldn't picture her being just part of his little stud band. Deep inside he had a feeling and a fear her health was somewhat fragile. This was more based on his feelings, than any fact. Perhaps it was based on his feeling of responsibility for changing her life at the wild band's watering hole. He wanted now to change her life again. Eager wondered about that.

Determined wanted to find, in the Golden State, a buyer for Bonita, someone really special who would love her and include her as part of his or her family. The buyer would need to be someone who would be willing to take care of her during the gestation period, knowing the coming foal would be his. He figured no well-established horse operation would put up with strings attached to a sale. He was looking for someone just starting out—with Bonita's class and ability she would be a showy asset. She would likely win or place pretty consistently, especially at the many breed competitions in that state.

On his last visit down there he was surprised to see the growth in the horse industry. There were little horse ranches springing up everywhere. Close to every town or city, someone established a place to house horses, fixing up a place with a few box stalls, an exercise area, and some little green summer pasture. The next thing anyone knew, there would be fifty box stalls, an indoor arena, and schooling shows would be held. Determined could picture Bonita on a little place like that. With her disposition, any family would love her as much as he and his family surely did.

When he had worked for the big outfits, mares weren't part of the remuda. Having his own spread to pay for made a big difference now. He needed to produce and market. Eager had told him some little starter stables would rather have a filly than a gelding. They figured they got better dividends on their investment. If the mare was showing and doing well, it could make the foals more valuable from the get-go.

Hoss listened to all the reasoning for Determined's drive to find Bonita a new home. He listened and kept his thoughts to himself. In his inner being, where he knew what his mind had not yet recorded, he knew Determined had to send Bonita away. The feeling had been building. The Snaffle Bit class finals cinched it. He had seen Determined's face when he left the arena. The togetherness Determined had experienced with Bonita in the class had both elated and frightened him. Bonita had become too important, too close. He couldn't stand the thought of anything coming between them. He wouldn't be able to take the pain of losing her. Vague "what ifs" had begun to rattle around in his thoughts. He had always heard it said and said it himself, "In every man's life he gets one good woman, one good horse and one good dog—if he is lucky."

Determined knew Bonita was sure enough his *one good horse*. It seemed to him by distancing himself from her he could keep forever this perfect closeness with his "good horse." That his decision was based on the false law of scarcity never entered the decision process. He did not realize it was possible to experience with all his horses some degree of the same closeness. He felt driven to move back to his "man in control world." He was missing the reality that the real world was created upon a grander scale.

That evening, Hoss and Eager helped Determined pack up and get ready to haul his horses back home. Eager's family would spend the night at the little cow ranch, then get an early morning start for California. Hoss figured the fair had lasted about long enough. It was expensive to hang around town. He was always glad to see his friends, but he would be glad to be back home.

Through that fall and winter, Determined spent a lot of time with Bonita. He spent more time on her grooming than he had in the past. He kept her in near-show shape. The first week home from the fair, he began to introduce her to the hackamore. He knew a new owner might want to show her in the hackamore classes. There were other little details he wanted to work on. In his talks with Eager, he had learned that some of the riders near Eager used quite a different method with their sliding stop. Determined wanted to prepare Bonita as much as he possibly could to fit into her new world—the world he had envisioned for her. Except for a little chirpy sound when he wanted more speed, he did not use voice commands with the horses he rode. He used more voice driving his team. He began to use more voice and to pretty much throw her head away in the sliding stop. It was sort of a fun experience. Some of the changes seemed to bother her at first. Soon it made very little difference. She would respond and perform about the same either way. Day by day, he was preparing her for her new home.

Winter was still lingering in Determined's area when he took Bonita to Fast Walker's place. Fast Walker knew his business and had the council of a good vet. Determined felt O.K. about leaving her, but because of the way the work had shaped up at the ranch, he left her there a little longer than he had planned. When Determined was able to make the trip to the southern part of the state for Bonita, it seemed like she had changed; somehow she seemed less of a filly. He was so pleased to see her and to see that she was in such good condition. Fast Walker said everyone who came around had asked about her. She was a showy little thing and now, bred to his stallion, she would be a great dam.

Throughout the winter Determined had kept in touch with Eager. Eager's role was to find the right buyer for Bonita. As early as the fall before, Eager had had a person in mind he felt could use and appreciate Bonita. He knew a couple just starting out in the horse business. They lived on an acreage on the outskirts of a growing city. The man of the family worked for a successful real estate firm. His second love was to build. He had a good set of carpenter tools, handed down from his grandfather, as well as the knowledge to use these tools— also handed down from his grandfather. Grandfather had been a carpenter by trade and this man of the house had spent many hours following his grandpa.

The love of horses and the drive to be involved with them came mostly from the woman of the family. Her family of origin had not been involved with horses. Her father had been a successful lawyer. He was active in local politics and interested in sports, particularly baseball. He had had a close and caring relationship with his daughter, whom he fondly called "Missy." When Missy was just past twelve years old, her dad had been killed instantly in an auto accident one deep foggy morning. He left for work and never came back. Missy was devastated. Her pain and grief were acute and lasted for many, many months. Finally, her mother and the doctor hit upon a plan to encourage her to again participate in her world. She was introduced to the world of horses. She began riding lessons under the tutelage of a very capable teacher.

Now, grown and married with one young daughter, it was her dream to build a business around horses. She still owned the first and only horse she had ever owned and he was something of a pensioner. She used him now to give lessons to small riders and for her own young daughter to ride. She had been away from participating in horse shows for several years and her dream was to find a good mare. She wanted a horse she could show, a horse with a really kind disposition, a family horse. She wanted to raise a foal with a good disposition. She had never started a colt, taken one through all the levels of training, but she had always wanted to. That was how Eager had become acquainted with her. He had started a colt for a friend of Missy. Since Missy was so interested in the process, she had asked to come along and observe. Eager had become well enough acquainted with her to realize she might be the ideal owner for Bonita.

Later in the spring, Determined was planning to show the Blue Roan in Reno. Missy and her man were interested in a chance to see Bonita. It was arranged that Determined would bring Bonita along with the Roan.

From the first moment Determined saw Missy, he could imagine her with Bonita. She was as tall or taller than he was and slender. She had a dusting of freckles, green eyes and hair the color of Bonita's coat. After Determined had shown her Bonita under saddle, he lengthened the stirrups for Missy. When she stepped on and rode off, it was a perfect fit.

14

It was Missy who led Bonita back to the stall and unsaddled her. She cooled her out and rubbed her down and talked gently to her. Determined visited with Man and watched, and was happy in his heart. He knew Bonita had the kind of new home he had imagined for her.

Old Mama remembered from the very beginning how she enjoyed the way Missy rubbed her down. She seemed to have a definite system—a rhythm. Bonita left the Sagebrush State early the next morning for her new life with Missy.

When the Chevy station wagon and homemade, two-horse trailer reached the great valley floor, it seemed spring had passed along and summer had caught up to them. They stopped for a few minutes under a grove of trees near a funny little orange-shaped fruit stand. Man bought some iced orange juice for himself and Missy. Missy unloaded Bonita and offered her a drink of cool water. Then Missy put a coin in the nearby pay phone. She called her mother who was caring for her little girl. Missy wanted them to know what time they would be arriving with the new family member. She was so excited.

When they drove up to the stables, Grandma and the little girl were there waiting. The little girl had the same basic coloring as her grandmother. She had brown hair and blue eyes. Missy's red hair had been a gift from her father's side of the family.

After unloading from the trailer, Bonita's first impression was one of heat. Having spent the first part of her life at the 5000 foot elevation level, being at nearly sea level, made her feel strangely lightheaded. Before the summer had passed, she realized her arrival had been during a cool spell in the great San Joaquin Valley.

She was glad to be out of the trailer. Missy and Man were so pleased to introduce her to the family. At nearly five, Girl was tall for her age, with all the excitement and curiosity typical of her age. Her grandmother, whom Girl called Nana, watched Girl with joy. Nana was interested in this new addition to the stables. She had encouraged Missy to purchase the filly; she had, in fact, financed the purchase. From the time Missy began to learn about horses, Nana had felt it was also important for her to learn as much as possible so she could really share with Missy. Nana had become quite capable in evaluating horses. When she looked at Bonita, she certainly liked what she saw.

Missy planned to repay Nana for the cost of Bonita with profits made from giving riding lessons. Nana didn't need the money, but being a prudent steward, she had basic attitudes about finances. The first ten percent she never considered belonged to her and immediately passed it to its Rightful Owner. The next ten percent went into a little passbook savings account at the bank. When it accumulated enough, she would move it over into other investments. Her husband had been interested in the stock market and had introduced her to it when they were first married. Having helped her learn about finances had been one of the many gifts he left her with at his sudden death. Later, Nana had educated Missy to have knowledge about and respect for money. Most of the money Nana saved now was invested in Girl's name. She wanted Girl to have broad choices when it came time for college.

Missy had stayed at home and gone to the local community college. She had continued to be active with her horses. At that time in her life, almost every weekend included some horse event or activity. Missy liked the stock horse events best, but she had shown in the pleasure and trail classes and since many events included English classes, she participated in those, too. She had trophies and blue ribbons to testify to her ability in a broad range of competitions.

Old Mama shifted her weight again. So many seasons had passed since she had come to live at Missy's. Some things seemed rather dim and far away in her memory. Other events almost seemed to have happened in the near past. How well she remembered her first moments with Girl, that part was easy to remember. When Girl walked up to her, she carried in her small hand a fist full of hay and in her eyes a look of excitement and joy. She walked right into Bonita's heart.

Bonita missed Determined and her other family, but her new family showered so much attention on her, she had little time to fret about the past. She had only been there a few days when Eager and his family came to visit. Eager was to help Missy learn to use the hackamore for Bonita. There were several county fairs in the late summer and fall that had Hackamore classes. If all went well between Bonita and Missy, they would be competing.

Before Bonita had left Determined's home, the vet had confirmed there would be a foal next year. About the only change that made for Bonita was how Missy's family thought of her. From the very beginning of her life with them, everyone called her Mama.

Back on Determined's outfit, the little bunch of brood mares had been treated more like the other stock. The mares were pasture bred and foaled out in the open. Each spring everyone was always excited to see the new foals. Mama's first foaling would be quite different. Missy would be very conscientious and concerned the whole time. A competent vet would be there when the time came; whether Mama needed him or not, Missy would need him. Mama's first foal was also to be Missy's first experience having a foal arrive at the stables. Through the years there would be many more, but firsts are often remembered as special.

Six weeks before the foal arrived, the vet had loaned Missy his university text to study in preparation for the event. Under any conditions Missy would have been concerned for the welfare of the mare and foal. Under the special conditions of Determined's sale, she was even more concerned. She realized her cost for the mare had taken into account the foaling and care for the colt that would return to Determined. She had made a wise investment. Determined had made an even better sale, for he had received dedication and devotion for Bonita's foal, far beyond monetary consideration. When Mama's actual foaling came, it was so routine, like the vet's textbook account of an ideal delivery.

Eager didn't really live near Missy, but he was close enough to drive there in the evenings after work. The summer days were long and daylight lasted. Man also took advantage of the extra light. They were expanding much of their facilities on a cash-and-carry basis. When payday arrived, Man would pull the horse trailer to the local lumber yard. He would use what cash he could afford to purchase materials to carry home. He usually was able to buy enough to keep him busy during the evenings for the next week. He made it a policy not to work on Sunday. Missy would watch him, in the late evenings, with his drafting paper and his master plan. When they had first moved to the acreage, they had worked for hours—planning each projected facility down to the last nail.

The summer Mama came, they were hoping to build Missy's tack room. At this time, Missy used a tack room across the arena from Mama's stall. Mama's stall was extra large, for it was to be a foaling stall. The tack room Missy used now she shared with two other riders, who were boarding their horses in her summer pastures. In the late fall these boarders planned to move across town where the facilities had an indoor arena and box stalls.

Man had planned from the beginning to build a special tack room just for Missy's gear. He intended to add some really nice, glassed-in cabinets for her trophies and the ribbons she had won, and the new ones Man was sure she would win. Mama had not been with them a month when Man closed a real estate deal with a sizable commission. He laughed and said, "Mama was a good-luck horse." The deal had seemed to fall from the sky. It was prime property that had been part of an estate held in trust. He found out about it just before it was to become available. At the time, he had a friend looking for just such a property. Since the commission was money beyond his penciled monthly budget, it became the "tack room." He had the lumberyard deliver all the materials at once—except for the interior furnishing needs.

Using his weekend and every minute after work, Man had framed the new tack room and gotten the roof trusses set. A good friend had given him a helping hand with that part. He had a three day weekend coming and really felt that would be an ideal time to close in the little building. Missy was so excited to be getting the new room.

Nana was planning to take a mini-holiday to the city. She wanted to take Girl along to show her the city sights: the Golden Gate Bridge, the harbor, and the wonderful zoo.

This plan worked well for Man's and Missy's work weekend. Without the little one to watch, they could devote every minute to their work project. The weather was warming up considerably and this holiday would give Nana and Girl a break from the heat. Missy liked the summer. Man usually found he could drink more fluids and wear fewer clothes and get by pretty well.

Early Friday morning, Nana and Girl left for the city. Man and Missy went right to the building task. Missy carried their picnic lunch to the job site. They took only a little break. It was almost closing time at the local drive-in, when they went for their evening meal. Driving home in the dusk, Missy felt so close to Man. She snuggled close and was drifting off to sleep by the time they reached home. They set the alarm clock an hour earlier for Saturday. Day was barely breaking when they were back on the job.

Since they had had a sturdy breakfast, they chose to eat fruit during the day. In a pair of blue jeans, Man's T-shirt and with her hair tucked up in a baseball cap, Missy could have passed for a young boy. Man thought she was quite the cutest carpenter's helper he had ever seen and she was good help, too. They made a great team.

The sun was setting when they took time out to barbeque a steak and grill some veggies. Missy really liked roasted ears cooked on the grill. The corn was the first of the season and very fresh. Man usually did the grill cooking but that night Missy did the honors while he hung the tack room door, making the new room complete except for the interior. When they put their paper plates in the garbage, it was back to work again. Man was so intent on completing the job, he couldn't seem to find a stopping spot.

Missy leaned against the interior of the room and watched him. The warm weather was getting to her. The evening air carried the sweet scent of her garden and she could smell grapes and figs. The four-o'clock, planted near the new tack room, perfumed the air. When she became aware of the sound of the doves, she left for the house. It was time to shower and be ready for bed. In his eagerness to finish the project, Man worked on. He was on the ladder with a hammer in his hand when he heard her return. He didn't turn from his work until she spoke. "Since you wouldn't come to bed, I've brought the bed to you."

She had! She had brought their camp bed and arranged it in the corner of the new room. Fresh from the shower with her auburn hair loose, Man knew she was the most beautiful woman in the world. Man dropped the hammer. It was indeed time for bed. They spent the night next door to Mama.

Six weeks later, as Missy was grooming Mama, she kept up her usual running conversation. But this time there was a special message. Mama was not the only expecting mama at the stables.

Missy and Mama continued to become closer friends. Everything seemed to be going well for them, except with the hackamore. Using the snaffle they were a great team, more than ready for competition. But for the county fair classes Missy wished to enter, they needed to find solutions to their problems with the use of the hackamore. Before Bonita left Determined's ranch, she had been responding well in the hackamore. Now she had begun to elevate her head. Missy realized she was somehow not getting things set up, in a meaningful way, for Mama. Missy thought about Determined and how he rode and communicated with Mama. Actually, they were so much in harmony, it was difficult to see anything but a well-balanced team. Determined was not very tall and was definitely bowlegged. He looked like Girl's doll, the one just made to sit astride the little toy horse and go everywhere together. Missy knew she and Mama were not making that sort of picture.

For Christmas the winter before, Nana had given Missy a new book. The first printing had been in 1950. A fellow in the North, a Doctor of Veterinary Medicine, had written it, but her own copy had been printed in 1958.

Missy spent extra hours in the evening rereading everything in the house that might give her a clue to her problem. She discontinued the use of the hackamore. Using the snaffle and concentrating totally on the way she was using her legs and body, things began to click again. By the time Eager came for another visit, she had quite decided to just enjoy Mama and forget about competing in the fall classes. Eager grinned. He didn't feel competition was quite that important anyway, especially not something to get really obsessed about. But, he had a surprise for Missy. He had made a soft leather hackamore; for a core he had used a piece of rawhide reata. Normally, he wouldn't have had such material for a core; however, a visiting pack rat in his temporary tack room had seen to it that his cherished reata was chewed into many useful pieces. He had brought the hackamore for Missy to try. If it worked for them, he would loan it to Missy for the season. He wasn't much for giving away the gear he made. It took too many hours to make.

Missy was never sure what worked. It could have been the soft new hackamore. It could have been the many hours of reading and imagining how she wanted things to work out. It could have been her attitude to forget and forgo the competition, or, as they say on other tests, all of the above. The exciting news for Missy was how she and Mama made a team in the hackamore events. Nana, Man and Girl came to watch the Stock Horse classes at the San Joaquin County Fair during a really hot spell. Missy was pleased with her ribbon of red. The next time she competed was a little further from home. Man went with Missy; Girl stayed with Nana. Eager and his family came to watch and cheer them on. The class performed in the evening with a nice breeze blowing and everything went well. Man carried the trophy to the car for Missy. It would fit nicely into the trophy case he had just completed in the tack room. Missy and Mama competed in six classes that fall. They brought home three blue, two red, and a "forgot to back up." It was more than Missy had hoped for.

Going into the fall, everything in Missy's life seemed to be more than she had ever hoped it could be. Her precious little girl was starting to school. Mama had more than fulfilled the dream as her "family" horse. Man had finished her new tack room. It had come into their life way ahead of schedule. The only thing that bothered Missy about the tack room was Man's decision not to give the 10 percent to the Rightful Owner. Man reasoned since the money for the tack room had been above their normal earnings, he would not count it in the usual way. This reasoning did not make sense to Missy. It seemed to her if the money was a gracious gift, it was even more important to say, "Thank You!" with the 10 percent, but she did not argue. She seldom fussed with Man. This fall she was so deliriously happy; she couldn't fuss with anyone about anything.

As the days grew shorter and the baby grew within, she became more convinced she was carrying a son. As a child, Man had been a towhead. He had not been the born-in-the-sun type, but rather a child who turned bronze from head to toe as he lived summer shoeless in cut off jeans. She hadn't known him then, but she had seen lots of pictures. She did not meet him until her second year at the local community college, where they shared some classes.

Missy had gotten her Associate of Arts in business. She had always loved her horses, but realized early she couldn't keep horses as a hobby in her adult life. She was grateful Nana had encouraged and supported her with horses in her youth. She wanted to combine that knowledge with sound business discipline.

15

Old Mama thought back to her first fall at Missy's. There had been a lot of activity around the stables for several months. She had left the stables on six occasions. Missy's attitude had made it easy for Mama to just go and do her best and not fret. She remembered going to shows with Missy. Missy's hair was the color of Mama's shining coat, and they made a pretty picture. Old Mama had to admit to herself she liked to be seen with Missy. She enjoyed the approving looks and comments. Well, maybe she was a little vain. Determined had let her know early on—"Some have it and some don't"—and that she really was special. Nothing in her life had ever caused her to think differently. In over a quarter of a century at Missy's, she had seen many changes around the stables but nothing had changed between herself and Missy. Now Missy had streaks of silver in her hair and Old Mama had gathered up quite a bit of white. They hadn't entered a competition for some time.

It was Boy and Golden Son's time at competition, the bronze young man who loved the sun and the golden palomino colt. They made a pretty picture together.

After that busy introduction to fall life at Missy's, winter was a surprise. Everything changed with the first heavy rain. There was a dreary thickness to the air. Sometimes the sun did not break through until nearly mid-day and some days not at all. After all these years, Old Mama still did not look forward to winter.

That first winter she was thankful for her large stall and

thankful for Missy. Girl was at school and Man was busy at work. Nana found other interests in the heavy weather, but Missy was faithful to see that Mama got plenty of exercise and care. During the long dreary winter, about the only other company Mama had was the visits Eager made to the stables.

Missy's new tack room was large enough to house a small work area in the corner. Eager was helping Missy cut leather and make her own soft hackamore. While they worked the leather, they talked horses. Eager told Missy the methods he had seen and some of the ideas he had tried. Some he wasn't very proud of, and he could tell her for sure that they did not work well over the long haul. Any physical restraint or gimmick would not give a rider any lasting way to communicate with the horse.

Just this last fall, when he had gone to the county fair to watch Determined and Dependable and visit Hoss, he had met a horseman from further north. They had had a little visit. This fellow was a wise one. Eager really couldn't say he knew what the fellow was about, but he was convinced there was something of value there to learn. There was a chance the man would be visiting near Eager's area sometime during the winter.

In more than a decade's experience around the show ring, Missy had observed some questionable ideas in action. One of the common practices that didn't seem right to her was working a horse against a fence to force him to turn, or riding into the back fence to force a sliding stop.

Once, while watching an early morning warm-up session with Girl, the quiet had been broken by Girl's little voice asking, "Mama, why is that man running the horse into the fence?" Since Missy had been wondering the same thing and did not have a ready answer for Girl, she took Girl to the snack bar for some hot chocolate.

Missy had a quick inquiring mind. It often seemed the responses she received from horse trainers were more evasions than answers. She came to feel the real answer was, "Because the other fellow did!" Missy had always been wary of the nameless "other fellow" and the "everybody does" guy.

When winter really came to stay, Missy had taken a seasonal break from most of her lessons. Since she did not have a covered arena, the mud became a problem. Missy and Man had plans for the covered arena, but that project was waiting. Missy's father had established a trust fund for Missy that would not be available for several years yet. When it became available, they would complete the larger buildings. In the meantime, Man and Missy continued to build, to plant their trees and shrubs, and to work at their landscaping. They were fortunate to live in an area where many folks they knew were avid gardeners and willing to share plant starts and gardening tips. A lot of work was required but only a little cash outlay. They studied their master plan in the evenings and planted their dreams during the day. Old Mama had been there to see the plants and the trees and the buildings rise.

That first spring at Missy's was as much of a surprise for Mama as winter had been. Spring came suddenly, or so it seemed to Mama. One morning the fog was just gone and the world turned a brilliant green. Hillsides and roadsides blazed with golden poppies. Miles of orchard blossoms joined the chorus and every bush, blade, and bird sang a salute to spring. In the mist of all that glory, Mama's first foal arrived: on time and easily.

Missy was so excited, she stuttered when she called to inform Determined. Determined said that from the beginning he had known it would be his future ranch stud. He was relieved to hear everything went well for Bonita. Determined was careful to formulate his thoughts along positive lines. He always fought to keep control of his thoughts. Deep inside was a doomsday voice he didn't dare let rise—a "what if," "yes but," "should have" voice. He felt this destructive demon was always lurking—waiting for a weak moment. He had no choice but to keep fighting to have control—control—control.

Missy had decided from the beginning she would not get too attached to Mama's baby. She had made plans to turn the two of them into a nearby hilly pasture so that their first months would give the foal a good start. The breeding fee had already been paid at a local stud farm and next season's foal would stay at Missy's. That would be the little one she would share with Mama. The rest of that spring and summer Mama didn't see a lot of Missy. When she came to visit the little hillside pasture, Mama was pleased to trot up and show off her son. Missy, too, had a new son to be proud of. With a mosquito netting securely fastened over an old hand-me-down buggy, that little fellow went wherever Missy went. He was nearby when she gave lessons, or cleaned stalls, or gardened.

Missy had more lessons to give this year. She gave credit for her increased business to the attention she had gotten showing Mama the fall before. The best advertising one can get is being seen receiving his or her own blue ribbon.

When late summer came, Eager went back to the county fair in the Sagebrush State. He hauled the young stud colt to Determined. Determined put him in the same stall Bonita had occupied. Even Determined's wife, who had not been well lately, came to say "Hello" to the colt. Determined was glad to have part of Bonita back. Although the foal resembled his sire in almost every way, Determined claimed he could look deeper and see Bonita.

With Mama's foal gone to Determined and Girl back in school, Missy began to think about riding Mama again. Nana was comfortable with caring for a little one of the age Boy was now. Mama and Missy had done so well in the Hackamore class, Missy was considering the Two-Rein class for their next project. Eager had shown her how and helped her make a hackamore, but on her own she had made a smaller version to use with the bridle. She had done the work secretly and it had not turned out quite like she would have liked. It could best be described as functional. When she hung it in her tack room, she hung it under the silver inlaid Garcia bit.

Missy was not in a hurry to push Mama into any competition, but sometime in the future she did hope to compete again. Not many horse shows offered a Two-Rein class, but there were a few. Missy felt if they worked some this fall and winter, maybe, after the second foal was weaned, there would be an opportunity to compete.

Missy was pleased Mama would foal again in the spring. She was really excited this would be her "keeping colt." She would be able to watch it through all the stages of its development. She so hoped this next foal would be a lot like Mama. She had chosen a gentle-natured stallion for breeding. Her priority in the new foal was for it to have a quiet, gentle nature. She was completely happy with everything about Mama, but in the new foal she was hoping for more size. The new sire stood almost sixteen hands and many of his colts had carried his size.

When she was busy working in the stables, Missy talked to Mama. She talked to her when she fed and groomed her. She talked to her when she came and went doing chores. She talked to Mama as she worked caring for the trees and flowers, while Mama watched from her run or exercise area. Missy had another little funny way; she whistled as she worked. There were several very peppy tunes Mama soon recognized. Sometimes Missy just whistled.

Mama had grown so close to Missy that she felt she knew everything in Missy's mind and heart. Everything except what was buried deep inside. Mama had no idea what Missy had buried. It did seem like lots of Missy's busyness worked as a cover for something she did not want to feel. Mama did not give lots of thought to that. It felt good to be back at the stables with Missy. Activities were picking up around the business. Man had made a large commission and borrowed the rest of what he needed to create a pole-construction, covered area between the two rows of box stalls with their outside runs. This was not a large arena but it would give them shade in the summer and dry footing in the winter. This construction was enough to encourage riders to board through the winter. Missy had more lessons that fall than she had had during the summer. It was okay with Mama. She liked to have folks coming and going.

One thing Mama had wondered about was that some riders obviously had a different attitude toward their horses than she remembered from her home on the ranch. Mama had noticed there were riders who became so completely obsessed with their horses there was little room in their lives for other relationships or other interests. This narrow focus kept these folks from fully participating in their own lives, so they missed out on much with their children and their spouses.

They did not see the spotlight glow about their child at the school sports event. They missed hearing the lines rendered at the school play. They were not there to taste the victory of the essay finished nor there to smell the embers of defeat in a project gone wrong. They were not there to feel the pain of lost dreams. Investing so much in their involvement with the horse, they invested little elsewhere. It is no secret that what a person puts first in his life dominates his existence. With the horse at the center of their world, these people made the horse their god; in so doing, Mama felt they diminished their world.

In her life with Determined, the horse had been important as part of the family operation. The horse had been a part of the working crew, part of the living, part of the life. Mama was comfortable with that attitude.

One Sunday, Eager came to visit. Missy didn't give lessons on Sunday. Eager's children came to say "Hello" to Bonita. They were growing up so fast. As every one gathered near Mama's stall, talk had turned to Eager's activities. In the winter before, he had had a quick visit from the fascinating fellow from the North. Eager had a good horse, a real handy prospect, but he was having problems with him. Well, he thought he was having problems with his horse. The fellow had given Eager some ideas on how to work things out. He had a really different approach to horse problems. He even referred to the problems as "people problems." Most of his suggestions focused on the rider working on himself or herself. Missy thought about the things Eager told her. She was open to learn. As more students and boarders became a part of her stables, she realized how many new questions and problems were surfacing.

16

When Old Mama remembered the second winter at Missy's, she thought how nice it had been to have more horses at the stables and more people coming and going. Mama liked people, maybe even better than horses. Mama thought about the lady with the short gray hair and merry laugh, she used to secretly share apples with Mama. Her horse fit her pretty well for size; he was a gelded Appy about fifteen hands, weighing a little less than eleven hundred pounds. He was not classy-looking but he was gentle. Most of the time all the lady wanted to do was love and feed him. She sometimes wanted to saddle up and walk, trot, and lope around the arena. She seldom went into the arena if there were more than two riders, counting herself. If anyone else came in to ride, she would leave and spend the last of her time grooming her Appy.

Occasionally, she would saddle up with the intention of riding out along the trail Man and Missy had constructed around the outside edge of their property. The trail was an easy ride. They had made it wide enough to drive a horse or a pony hitched to a cart. The Merry Laugh Lady didn't want much from her horse. It quite irritated Mama when Appy wouldn't even do willingly what few things Merry Laugh asked of him. Merry Laugh was a timid, anxious rider who had longed for a horse of her own when she was twelve years old. Her father's job at the local garage met the needs of his family of four children, but a horse was not a need. Merry had married early and raised a family of three children who were now all grown and raising families of their own. At the age of sixty-two, Merry had acquired her first horse, Appy.

Old Mama thought about the first morning she and Missy had had to rescue Merry. Well, maybe support, was a better term than rescue. It was indeed a grand morning. The weather was warm and still. Missy and Mama were planning on a ride out along the trail. Missy had a secret from the other riders. In the back of the property, where the trail skirted some willows, Missy had a pass-through gate. She had an arrangement with a neighbor to pass through his field and then she and Mama could ride down along the river. Missy had been riding there since they first acquired their property. She was thankful to have the extra space. To repay for the privilege, she would watch the stock the owner occasionally pastured there. That day Missy was whistling a happy tune as she prepared to leave the stables.

Merry was preparing to leave the stables, too, but Appy was not prepared to go anywhere. From across the arena it almost seemed Appy's feet were permanently fastened to the soil, unless, of course, Merry headed him toward his stall. Missy stopped whistling long enough to call to Merry just to wait up a minute. Missy didn't make a big deal of it. She just rode over, moved Mama up beside Appy, took hold of his bridle, and rode a ways with them. Appy was very gentle and once on the trail he went along quite willingly. Mama couldn't understand why he would want to treat his kind owner so unkindly. This became something of a routine that fall.

Merry worked in a pink uniform as a volunteer several mornings a week for the local hospital. This gave her only two mornings a week to ride out along the trail. Mama figured that was about the correct amount of time. She liked Merry, and Missy seemed to enjoy riding with her and explaining things to her. Actually, these mornings became lesson-time for Missy and Merry.

Mama liked best the morning rides when she and Missy

escaped off the property and rode the river pasture. Those rides seemed freer, more like her rides with Determined. She thought about her foal growing up at Determined's, and she pictured the routine there and the things he would be experiencing. She felt he would be one who would like the sagebrush and the wide-open spaces. Sometimes she missed the mile upon mile of beckoning openness. Deep inside, it gave her a quiet, peaceful feeling to be able to "look two days in any direction," as Hoss used to say.

Old Mama thought about that life far from town. It had been a joy. The other side of that was the distance from medical help when things went wrong. How frightening it had been for everyone when Determined had been burned so badly. There had come a time in her life when it was fortunate the veterinarian was not far away. But that was a very long time after her second year at Missy's.

During their rides Missy was able to encourage Merry to use her legs as something besides a way to stay in the saddle. As Merry improved, she commented that it seemed more difficult to acquire riding skills than she had imagined it would. Maybe the fifty years from her first dream of being a horse owner had made some differences. Merry watched Missy's other new boarder and marveled how easy everything was for her. This young girl was about thirteen and she rode a happy horse. She was a boarder only, as she couldn't afford lessons. She didn't really need any, as her horse did willingly nearly everything she asked of him. Most of the time she rode bareback with just a halter. Since she was always wherever Missy was, she was usually the one to volunteer to deliver to anyone messages that were received on the stable's phone. Missy called her Miss Messenger. Miss Messenger's horse was much younger than Missy would have suggested for a young rider. He was pretty much a colt, and the girl had done all his gentling. For size, he was just past pony scale and his breeding looked like open range-mix. The most noticeable thing about those two was how completely happy they seemed together. Merry watched them and wondered if she would ever reach that level of riding. She realized the riders who thought about levels of riding usually had another picture in mind, but Merry just wanted a happy horse she could enjoy riding away from the barn as well as towards the barn.

Just before the pumpkins ripened outside the end of Mama's run, a new person was introduced at the stables. Actually, he was one-half the size of a grown person with two and one-half times the energy of any adult. He came to take lessons on Missy's older lesson horse. He thought he wanted to be a cowboy. He wanted to own his own horse and gear. However, his parents thought it wiser to start with lessons and proceed from there. For his first lesson, Energy came promptly on time. After his first session Energy came earlier each time and was picked up somewhat later from each lesson. The regular boarders usually didn't get well acquainted with the lesson riders but Energy was an exception. He was around almost enough to be a nuisance. It was like Mama felt and Missy and Merry said, "That little fellow grows on a person," until finally it didn't seem quite right if Energy was gone.

During the school break after the turkey day, a suit-and-tie father and a well-dressed mother came to visit Missy's stables. Missy's tack room was still decorated with a handprint turkey made by Girl. The couple brought their slender, brown-haired, hazel-eyed daughter who was in her second year of high school and quite serious about her riding. She had been riding at another stable across town since she was nine. She had progressed from riding lessons on stable-owned horses to a lease arrangement for two years, and had owned her own Thoroughbred mare for several years. Her parents were happy with the arrangements she had had, but since they were moving to a new home near Missy, they were looking for a more convenient place to board the mare. They had a lot of questions, but apparently Missy passed the test. A few days after their visit, they called to make arrangements to move the mare at the first of the month.

Even though the weather was dense and gloomy, things stayed quite active around the stables. From the day she arrived with her horse, the brown-haired teenager came at least four times a week to ride. She was pleased with her tall, bay Thoroughbred most of the time. She nearly always felt good about their rail work in the arena, but the outside trail was quite a different experience. It usually went from bad to worse. The horse would leave the barn area without a fuss, but the return part of the ride wasn't any fun. It bothered the serious girl terribly. The more it bothered her to have the horse taking control and "jigging" all the way home, the worse the horse wanted to jig along and not walk. Missy began to be available to ride out with Serious whenever possible. This wasn't a paid lesson, just relief and support for the girl. This support relieved the situation temporarily but did not cure anything. With Mama and Missy beside her, the Thoroughbred would relax and extend into a beautiful ground-covering walk. A solo trip on the trail, however, was no fun at all. The young girl would return nearly in tears. Mama felt sorry for her. Mama had never put a rider through that much pain. Although that was true, Mama did not realize that in her two-owner life span she had been owned and loved by two way-above-average riders.

Before the Thoroughbred had been there two weeks, another bay came to board. This mare was something different. She was about nine-years old. Her owner said he had bought her as a half-starved yearling at the Saturday night sale. Well, Mama didn't think she looked like she had missed any meals since then. She was plenty round. The jovial fellow who owned her was pretty sure she was part Morgan, but he was unsure about the rest of her pedigree. Jovial had raised her and trained her to pull a little yellow cart. She was very dependable with the cart but she was not quite as well mannered when he rode her. Her stall was on the same side of the arena as Mama, down on the end. Missy had assigned them an end stall so the little cart and equipment could be stored nearby. Jovial was happy with the arrangement and he and his horse were a welcome addition to the stable's family. When Nana, Girl, and Boy came to visit the stables, he gave them rides in the cart. Merry even went for a drive with him down around the trail.

All the horses except for Serious' horse got used to seeing the cart on the trail. Serious' horse did not like that yellow contraption, so they worked out a schedule not to share space. That wasn't difficult because Serious seldom rode the trail, and Jovial never used the arena for a place to drive. About once or twice a week he rode in the arena. Usually, the school-age children weren't around when he rode. He had difficulties when he rode that he never experienced while driving. He tried to use the arena when he was the only rider. Merry realized early on that he wanted space so she did not use her two-horse occupancy rule with him. If his horse were saddled to ride, her horse got extra grooming. One morning, she groomed her horse for over an hour. She tried to watch Jovial without being too obvious that she was watching. He had entered the arena without closing the end gate. The very first pass around the arena his mare tried to duck out the gate. Merry could not see what Jovial was trying to accomplish, but when he and his horse left the arena they both were sweating as though they had had a good workout. Neither one looked very happy. She knew the feeling. She and her horse still had not worked out the "leave-the-barn" issue.

All the children were out of school on a brief holiday when Mama's second foal arrived. Missy had her veterinary friend in attendance but again he was only needed to support Missy. Mama had an easy foaling for her first filly.

Girl had a feel for and enjoyed using words with many syllables. She described the new foal as gorgeous when Nana asked her about it. From that time on, the filly was called Gorgeous even though her registered name was different. Mama and her foal stayed around the stables for a longer time this foaling. Missy had decided not to breed Mama back again as soon as last time, because she wanted to have some time to get well acquainted with the foal. Truthfully, Missy felt a little possessive about this foal. She did not want anyone else to be handling her or be responsible for Gorgeous. Missy thought she and Mama could just be the foal's principle providers and companions.

17

With Mama and the new foal close by, Missy thoroughly enjoyed that spring. She had made plans to turn them out into the little hillside pasture but that would come later. She spent a lot of mornings, when she didn't have lessons, getting Gorgeous to come to her for scratching. Mama was helpful in getting the baby to accept Missy. Mama was more aloof with the other folks at the stables. Most of them came by everyday to say "Hello," but only Missy went inside Mama's stall or run.

Before Mama and the baby left for the hillside pasture, a new boarder came to the stables. Mama looked him over. She thought he really had pretty eyes. He was a little on the thin side but his gray coat was shiny and immaculate. She would have been more favorably impressed if he had not been such a nervous sort. It was pretty obvious his owner was nervous, too. It was also obvious that she loved her horse. She had the horse's pedigree memorized, clear back across the ocean to his ancestors on the desert. Missy and Mama were impressed with her memory, if not his pedigree.

Along about then, Mama and Missy were surprised by a visit from Eager. They didn't see much of Eager since he had taken a new job. He was so busy he was even working on this day. He was driving his boss's rig to pick up a couple of mares the boss had sent out to breed. When questioned, he said everyone at his home was okay. They were all busy. His kids had school sports and 4-H projects and all sorts of things going on. He didn't have much time but he did take the time to look at Bonita's baby. He went into the stall with Bonita and the baby. He stood quietly just inside the door. Bonita edged away from him and the young one crowded against her side away from Eager. Eager waited, watching intently. He talked to Bonita and watched to see what she was saying with her body in answer. In the beginning the curve in her body formed a cove of protection for her colt. She knew Eager but she didn't know yet if it was okay for him to be really close to her foal.

Missy watched from outside the stall. As Eager talked to Mama, her body relaxed a little and her weight shifted to the side away from Eager. If she felt secure enough, she might move towards Eager. Watching closely, Missy realized Eager too had moved. He had shifted his body life back a little, away from the mare. It was as if he had said, "It's okay, I will not force myself upon you, but you can come; the choice is yours."

Missy watched closely to determine if Eager was attempting to fake Mama out. Many times she had seen people set up to gain an animal's confidence, only to use the situation to complete their project without regards for the animal's ultimate understanding or frame of mind. Missy had spent the last several years getting acquainted with Eager. Now that he was between her and her precious foal she didn't know if she knew him at all. Missy could sense Mama was not sure if she knew him either. Oh, they knew who he was on the outside. They were not sure who he was on the inside. They were on alert to protect the foal. Missy was surprised at her own feelings. If he made one move to upset Mama and the foal, she would ask him to leave the stall. She had put in too much time getting the foal to accept her to allow any reversal now.

She moved closer to the stall door and waited. Eager moved not forward or back. He simply shifted his weight to the other leg. He extended his hand palm up toward Bonita. Bonita raised her left front foot and set it back down in her track. Eager grinned and stepped back out of the stall. "You're a real good Mama," he told Bonita. He addressed himself to Missy, "There was a time when I would never have left the stall without handling the foal." Missy was thankful that wasn't now.

Missy walked with him to his rig, but as soon as he had driven out of sight, she returned to Mama and Gorgeous. She wanted to be reassured the confidence the little one had built up towards her was still intact. When she opened the stall door and stepped in with Mama, she laughed out loud; she couldn't help it. She leaned against the stall door and laughed. Mama was standing right where Eager had left her; peeking out from behind was Gorgeous' little head. Something in the body language caused Missy to see them as a fluffed-up mother hen and her protected chick. Missy's laugh broke the spell. Mama and her baby came to visit Missy. What a delight they were to Missy! Again, she was struck by the wonder of it all. How much—how very much—animals would share with you and teach you, if you just let them.

She thought about Eager and the way his attitudes were changing. He had always been what the cowboys referred to as "a good hand." He had had lots of experience with horses of various natures. Since he had become acquainted with the gentleman from up north, he was getting a different picture of horse-man relationships. She was thankful he was willing to visit about it and to share what he was learning.

Later that day while Missy was working with her young lesson riders, she watched the nervous gray and his rider. The horse was really a gentle one. Missy based that observation on the fact he did not bolt and run away, didn't buck, strike, or kick. Still, it did not look like he and his nervous rider were having much fun. Nervous was tense and unhappy-appearing as she continually tried to get the gray to quiet down. She had been just outside the arena the whole time of the lesson. It appeared she wanted to sit quietly on gray. Gray would have none of that. Nervous kept after the horse. She kept getting after him to stand still. It looked like she couldn't stand his moving and he couldn't stand still. It gave Missy the urge to "send them to the showers." Now, she could appreciate her gym teachers' reaction to some of the gym class confusion.

Missy thought about Eager. It might work out if she could ask him to do a special workshop session here at the stables. It would be worth a try to see if he could come and observe. It would be great if someone could help these riders.

Missy did not see much of Eager throughout the rest of the summer. She and Man took their children to the local county fair. Although she was not competing, Missy wanted to see the Stock Horse classes. Eager was competing on a Hackamore horse. The two families shared lunch at the Snack Shack. This gave Missy the opportunity to ask some questions and to share how well things were going at the stables. Miss Messenger had taken her horse out to stay at a relative's ranch. There she had more places to ride and some cousins to ride with her. She was such a lively person to have around that everyone missed her, but her stall was not vacant long. A petite blonde, whose mount was also small, took Miss Messenger's place. Her horse was a chrome sorrel with some Arab blood. This little blonde rider was very capable. She liked to show in the smaller local competitions. She rode in both Western and English classes. Her grandfather drove her to and from the stables and paid her expenses. He affectionately called her Teeny. Soon, everyone at the stables used her nickname, as it seemed to fit so well. Teeny was an energetic, forward-motion, rider. The problem she was having was understanding how to get her horse to backup. Missy asked Eager about the backing problem. He gave her some ideas to try. He mentioned how hard it was to know what exactly to suggest when he was not there to observe the horse and rider together. This gave Missy the opening that she had been hoping would come about.

Missy mentioned some of the other riders' problems. She asked Eager if he might come help the group if they could all arrange their time for a session some Sunday in the fall. It was agreed they would work towards a gathering at Missy's in the fall. Eager said he was real busy and wouldn't be going out-of-state to the fair this year. He would miss visiting Determined and seeing all his other friends. It would likely be around that time he could find a free Sunday.

Missy was excited the next day at the stables to be able to tell everyone about the plans for a schooling session coming up in the fall. It would be a real opportunity to get some help for the problems that were keeping everyone from truly being able to enjoy time with their horses.

Man and Missy talked it over. Man thought if Eager was willing to help, then it should be financially worth his time. It was decided Missy would call around and see if some of her other friends with horses would like to come and get help with their problems. A close friend of Missy's worked with a 4-H horse group. She had a teenage son and daughter who had been riding for some time. Since they lived in a more rural district, they often had an opportunity to help neighboring ranchers with their cattle. They liked to help brand or gather and move cattle from one field to another.

For several years their family had kept a brood mare on the place. This gentle-natured mare had produced foals for each of the young riders. It was pretty exciting to have young colts to start. The problem was they had the colts, but didn't really have the experience to get them started right. They had received some help and suggestions from the neighboring rancher friends, and their love of the colts had gotten the colts mauled around and quite gentle. They said they didn't buck or spook from the saddling. However, Brother's brown gelding still would not just stand quiet to be saddled. Sister had started the two-year old. Her filly looked almost identical to her brother's gelding except for being smaller and two years younger. She was a jewel to catch and saddle, but when Sister rode her down the arena, the filly carried her head off to the right. Sister did not know what was causing or how to correct this awkward habit. When they heard about Eager coming to Missy's, they were more than thrilled to be included. After thinking it over, their mom decided she would bring along a horse to ride, also. She had several questions that came up when she worked with her 4-H kids. Maybe, after the session with Eager's group, she would be able to better help her members.

During this summer's building, Man had constructed a snack bar area with a little covered patio. Everyone talked it over and it was decided to have a potluck during the day of the lessons. The new patio would be initiated. More time could be applied to the sessions if no one left the grounds in search of food or drinks. It would likely be a pretty warm day, so they planned for lots of ice tea and lemonade.

Missy was happy that she would have Mama to ride when Eager came for the lessons. Gorgeous would be weaned and living across the valley in the foothills with a couple other weanlings and an old babysitter mare. The foothills pasture privilege came through a friend of hers who had made all the arrangements. Missy had been searching for a place to turn Gorgeous out where she would have the advantage of learning to travel in rougher terrain. This was the fall Missy wanted to work towards exhibiting Mama in the Two Reined classes at some county fairs.

Missy brought Mama home about ten days before Eager was to come. Things went so well with Missy and Mama that she almost forgot anyone else had problems. It seemed wherever Missy wanted to go or whatever she wanted to do, Mama was happy to be going there or doing that. It almost seemed she had advanced in every way during her pasture stay. Whatever Missy asked her to do, she seemed to understand what was expected of her. It did not seem to matter if Missy used her snaffle bit, the hackamore, or her two-rein set-up. What-ever Missy used, Mama seemed completely content.

With everything going so well between them, Missy be-gan to think about getting in some cattle for practice work. The fellow with the river pasture called about then to ask Missy about checking on some young stock he was adding to his pasture. Missy bravely asked for the temporary loan of three or four to use with Mama. This was not a problem. Mama was a natural with cattle. They did not need much practice time.

18

When the day came for Eager's class, Man and Missy decided it would be a good investment to have a sitter come to the house for Boy. Missy decided not to saddle up Mama. Things had been going so well with them it didn't seem necessary. Man and Missy had decided earlier that ten riders would be a good-sized group. In order to complete the group of ten riders, they decided to pay for Girl to participate.

Missy told Mama she was not being left out; from her stall she could observe the whole arena. In fact, she had a premium ringside seat for the event.

Serious was the first one to show up at the stables. She was there saddled two hours before the class was to begin. Merry and Teeny arrived about the same time, both stayed busy grooming until it was almost time to begin. Nervous brought a friend with her who helped her with her grooming and saddling chores. Jovial and Energy arrived anxious for the class to start. Jovial intended to ride in the class and to get some help with the problem he referred to as "escape." For months now he had been careful to close the arena gate while he rode. He didn't feel his problem was cured but it was prevented for the present. Missy's friend, the 4-H leader, arrived driving a small stock truck. They had had a little trouble getting started from home, as Sister's filly was hesitant to load. Missy waited until almost time for Eager to arrive to saddle the lesson horses for Energy and Girl.

Earlier, Energy had reached the stage in his riding where he was to catch and saddle the lesson horse by himself. When he first began to do it, things had gone fairly smoothly. Lately, however, Lesson Horse had been giving Energy a problem. As Energy reached to bridle him, he would elevate his head. Before the habit had progressed too far, Missy had taken back that part of the routine. Since Lesson Horse's giraffe act was a real frustration to Energy that was what his question to Eager would be. Energy's parents planned to be there to watch him. Since they had plans for later in the afternoon, he would be the first one Eager would help.

Missy had chosen not to ride because she wanted to be sure everything went well. Several of the riders were bringing family members to watch. She was expecting Eager to bring his family. She felt responsible, as the hostess, to see that everyone was reasonably comfortable. Nana would be there and she was comfortable with any size of group. She was a natural at the meet-and-greet ritual. It was easy for her to see that everything went smoothly. She seemed able to anticipate what was needed before there was a need. Missy tried to learn from her Mother but when it came to "crowd control," as she referred to it, she was still in the "why didn't I think of that" stage.

When Eager arrived, it was a little past the scheduled starting time so Missy hurriedly introduced him. She left him on his own to introduce his philosophy about the horse. Missy was surprised how bothered he seemed. In the time she had known him it had always appeared he was quite confident. In small groups or one-on-one, it was easy to say what he felt, but this larger group caused him to feel like he was on the stage and he definitely had "stage fright." Missy was considering some way to rescue him when he solved the issue on his own. With a big grin he said, "Well, now you all know me. I need to know you. Starting here on my left, tell me who you are and tell me your horse's story."

Nervous went first and recited her horse's pedigree and the bottom line was the horse wouldn't stand still. Merry's horse wouldn't leave the barn. Serious' horse wouldn't walk coming back to the barn. Teeny's horse wouldn't back up. Jovial's horse wouldn't go past an open gate without trying to duck out. Energy's horse wouldn't put its head down for the bridle. Brother's horse wouldn't stand to saddle. Sister's filly wouldn't travel straight. Girl just loved her horse and didn't know if she even had a problem. Club Leader Mom was interested in all the problems since she saw them all, at one time or another, with her own 4-H Club members.

Eager started from there. He said that although they all had a different problem, they all had the same problem. There was an obvious lack of communication between horse and rider. He realized the riders felt they had a problem with their horses. It did appear that way. Eager said he had been getting acquainted with a fellow whose approach was different. This fellow's attitude was, "The people think they have a horse problem, but really the horse has a people problem." Eager said the class would spend some time trying to determine where the horse was having its "people problem." The idea he wanted everyone to grasp was that he was not there to help them work on their horse. He was going to help them get started working on themselves. He wanted each rider to recognize what was going on with his or her horse. The rider would take the responsibility to learn from the horse.

These were not new ideas and attitudes for Missy but she could tell there was a mood change in the group. It was as though a hot summer breeze had blown through the arena. A wilted, confused appearance settled over the riders, except for Energy and Girl. If Girl had a problem, she had no knowledge of it. Energy, on the other hand, still knew he had a problem or at least the two of them had a problem. He was pretty sure if he were taller, like Missy, there wouldn't be a problem at all. So he defined his problem for Eager as the fact he was too short to bridle his horse.

When Eager asked him to come forward out of the group

and demonstrate, he was more than ready to prove his theory. It sure looked like he was right. Bridling that horse from where that ten-year old stood seemed about half a person too short. Every time the youngster reached for the horse, Old Lesson Horse would elevate his head. Eager allowed the demonstration to go on long enough for the group to get a fair picture of what was happening. Energy would put some pressure on Old Lesson Horse, intending to bring the horse's head down, but when the horse would elevate, Energy would immediately release the pressure. The youngster didn't want the horse's head to go higher so he would release all pressure and attempt to start again. Each new start was a higher reach. Old Lesson Horse looked like he was ready for a circus giraffe act. The child was becoming more frustrated with each attempt.

As Eager approached the situation, Energy stepped back to give him his position and problem. Eager surprised the assembly by dropping to his knees, which made him about the same height as Energy. When he made as if to bring the horse's head down, Old Lesson Horse went up, but Eager did not release as the boy had done. He kept some pressure and Old Lesson Horse dropped his head down, away from the pressure. Eager gave the horse an immediate reward by releasing all pressure. Then he set it up again. With each new start, the horse put his head further down. In moments, that old horse had his nose nearly on the ground. This made it almost too easy to bridle him. Little Energy had a wide grin as he got the picture. Eager turned the bridling back to the boy. Energy successfully bridled, unbridled, and rebridled Old Lesson Horse. A little applause from the group was further reward for Energy. The boy, the teacher, and the horse all looked happy. Missy was delighted. She thought about the old saying, "A picture is worth a thousand words." This was surely a million dollar picture.

Eager had everyone's complete attention and while he had their attention, he told them they would all be working with the idea of setting things up for the horse so that the wrong things were difficult and the right things were easy. The wrong thing was whatever the rider did not want the horse to do; the right thing was what was desired. The group began to come to life as though the air was now a clear, cool, evening breeze, even though it was really still a very warm afternoon.

Before the group session had started, Missy had handed Eager an envelope with the money she had collected. It was to be a group session but each rider would have individual attention. Missy had written on the envelope a suggested lineup order for the individual work. Energy was first because his folks had to leave for a company picnic. She had suggested Nervous go second, to relieve Nervous and her horse from the pressure of waiting and also to relieve the rest of the group who had to share their nervous energy. Eager had been studying Nervous and her influence on the group. Teenys' horse had come with Teeny and was staying with her. Merry was quite awake but her horse had gone to sleep. Jovial was off at the far edge of the group quite comfortable. Girl's dear old lesson horse was not wasting any energy, but the nervous gray horse seemed to be striking a nerve in Serious' Thoroughbred and Brother and Sister's colts. The colts were lined up near 4-H Leader's quiet mount and this helped buffer the tension for them. With the tight time schedule and the newness of the group, it seemed a good idea to work with Nervous and her horse.

Before Eager called on Nervous to work with her horse, he felt like he needed to address the whole group. In some way he wanted to impress upon them how really sensitive horses can be. Each horse is unique. No two horses are alike, any more than the riders are alike. Eager felt that was great. He wanted to impress upon them how much the rider's attitude and frame of mind was reflected in his horse. If the rider is unsure or worried, likely the horse feels it intently. The horse can become worried and unsure, too.

One of the quotes Eager had picked up from his new mentor was "Adjust to fit the situation." It was a very important concept in working with the horse. Eager reminded himself how equally important it was in helping the riders. This next rider was nervous and so was her horse. Being the focus of the group was not going to calm either one of them. When he called her forward, she identified her problem. Eager asked if she would like him to ride her horse to demonstrate some things on which she could possibly work. She was visibly relieved and immediately dismounted and began to help adjust the stirrups.

Eager kept his body quiet and the gray immediately responded with less activity. As the horse moved, Eager moved with the horse, picking the horse's feet up and setting them down. They began to move in a circle, first one direction and then the other. While this was going on, Eager was counseling the group about making use of the energy the horse has to offer. He told them not to discourage the horse from moving, not to be getting after the horse to stand still, but use the energy to learn to move together. In a very short time the gray horse stopped wanting to move. Eager immediately gave him lots of slack in the reins and sat quietly. It must have felt good to the gray who gave himself a little shake and blew out his nostrils almost as if to say, "So There!" Everyone laughed. Eager dismounted. Nervous led her relaxed horse to his stall. It might be some time before Nervous would understand what had happened between the horse and the man, but she had seen things could be different.

Eager wanted to work with the colts next. He had Brother come forward and remove the saddle, then saddle the colt as if he were at home. Eager was observing, looking to see if the colt was still spooky or what was going on. Actually, he was quite impressed with the young fellow and the horse's attitude. The saddling problem appeared to be the handler's failure to understand when the horse was getting ready to move.

Brother needed to be more on guard to block the moves before the horse started. Eager asked if the young man cared if he worked with his horse to demonstrate how to block these unwanted moves. In a short time Brother was able to change places again with Eager and was able to head off the unwanted moves. Eager explained what they were doing was effective because the horse understood better what was expected of him. He complemented the young fellow on such a good job with his horse. He had such a good foundation it only took a minor adjustment to make things easier for the horse and rider.

Working with a group of riders and addressing individual concerns was something of a time stretch in a single session. The attention moved to Sister's filly. The young girl had done a good job of starting her filly with her brother's help. The filly was not at all spooky or hard to handle. She would stand for just about anything. The problem Sister was having with her filly's head position had just recently started. The girl was hoping to figure out why her filly was traveling with her head off to the right. As she demonstrated her problem, Eager asked her to do a little more with her left leg and left rein. He asked her to try to feel where the life was coming through the horse's body. He cautioned her not to make a big issue of their problem. This gave him the opportunity to remind the group how important it was to recognize and reward even the slightest try or the smallest change. In very little time everyone could see a change in her filly.

Eager looked at Merry's mount. It was nodding off again. He asked Missy if she would be willing to ride Merry's Appy, if Merry was comfortable with that, in order to make it easier for Merry to see what needed to be done. He didn't feel leaving the barn would be a big issue, but Appy didn't have a lot of life in his feet, or anywhere else just now. Since Missy gave Merry lessons, it should work to give Missy the experience to pass along later.

The class had a short break while Missy put her saddle on Merry's horse. Eager instructed Missy not to try to take the horse away from the barn. He asked her to do whatever she needed to do to keep the horse's feet moving. Missy moved with Appy up and down and around near the barn. When he slowed as if to stop, she would be more energetic in her body and legs. Since Missy was not directing the horse, the horse seemed to realize he could go further from the barn. He went out a ways, slowed down, and seemed to ask if he could stop now. They stopped, settled there a few moments, and then he turned and traveled towards the barn. Missy went right along with a lively rhythm that encouraged movement. Again, they milled around near the barn in constant motion. This was too much like work for the horse. Appy left home, just walked off away from that old barn. He went further than the time before, and then he asked to stop. He waited longer away from the barn. Then he took another journey back to the barn, but he left sooner this time and he took the trail without asking to stop. Missy went with him and they disappeared down the trail.

At this point, Eager took the opportunity to emphasize again for the students the concept of setting things up so the wrong thing is difficult and the right thing easy. Merry didn't want the horse to hang around the barn. She wanted the horse to go with her down the trail. When Missy, riding for Merry, did not try to leave the barn area but kept the horse's feet in constant motion, this was mentally and physically difficult for the horse. It was easier for the horse to go down the trail than to hang around the barn. Since Missy didn't want to miss anything while she was out on the trail, she came fast-walking back in no time. Missy gave Merry back her horse to take care of and settled herself on the arena fence.

Teeny and her little sorrel horse became the next project. Teeny was a young energetic rider with a happy horse. The two of them had no problem with impulsion. They would walk together, trot together or getty-up-and-go in unison. If Teeny wanted to slow down and stop, they would shut it down. But somewhere in all the forward motion, Teeny couldn't find a reverse. When Eager asked, she explained, "She could go from low to overdrive in record speed, stop on a dime like her Grandpa said, but there was no reverse." She mostly made small circles and changed directions. Backing was not fun, just a drag for her and her horse.

Eager asked her if she minded if he got on her horse to give her a clearer picture of the problem. Better yet, he suggested, would be to demonstrate on a more seasoned horse. Missy took the hint and went to saddle Mama. She could tell the talking and walking was making a long afternoon for Eager. While she was gone, he talked about backing. Eager said he had watched loose horses in a coral or pasture and had not observed them backing much at all, although he had observed on occasions when another horse made an aggressive move, a horse might have to back to escape injury.

He was glad to see Bonita saddled and ready. He and little Bonita went back a long ways. She was surely one of his favorite horses. When he settled into the saddle, he asked the group to watch the saddle horn. He did not pick up the reins. In fact, he crossed his arms in a relaxed manner.

As his body came alive and he felt Bonita and thought about preparing to back, the saddle horn shifted back. Some of the group saw it move, some missed it. He set it up again; Bonita started the life backwards in her body. This time the group was ready. Eager began to move backwards with Bonita. His legs were backing in rhythm with Bonita's, even though his movements were not obvious to the group. As he backed, he told the group how important it was to get the horse ready, to let your idea become the horse's idea. He stopped Bonita with his body, and then squeezed her to move forward again.

After they returned to their starting position, they stopped beside Teeny. This gave Eager the opportunity to visit with Teeny. He encouraged her to pick up on her reins and wait for her horse to give to her. Her horse's first trip was a barely visible weight shift back. Eager was able to point this out to Teeny and help her with her timing so she could reward her horse. Sitting near Teeny, he was able to help her realize how to prepare the horse to back. It helped both Teeny and her horse when he suggested it might help to exaggerate some body movements just to get some understanding. Teeny began to shift the top of her body back, and her horse moved back under her weight. Everything was being done in slow motion so the group was able to see what was helping. This gave Teeny something to build onto in the future.

Eager realized having Teeny shift the top of her body back in order to get the backing picture could seem wrong to some riders. Shifting back, did, in fact, cause the weight to be over the very place on the horse's back a rider would want to lighten up. So much of what Eager suggested for the rider to do depended on the circumstances at that very moment. This was the reason he found it so difficult to try to help with any problem. Teeny was a young rider with much life in her body; every fiber was set on forward. She and her horse had been operating that way for a very long time.

When Serious questioned Eager's coaching of Teeny's backing, Eager had Teeny try putting a little weight in the stirrups to lighten the back. Neither Teeny nor her horse could make a mental separation and connect this with backing. They were immediately in forward motion again. Then he asked them to stop all motion. Stopping all motion was very difficult for that pair. Since Teeny and her horse had been living with their problem for some time, it would take some exploring on Teeny's part to find her answer. Eager encouraged her to stop completely more often and shift into reverse if only for one step. Then they could built upon this experience.

Everyone cleared the arena and lined up outside for the next project. Jovial rode in and left the gate open. Eager noticed Jovial had a really nice way with his hands. He was sensitive to his horse. When the situation presented itself and Jovial's horse was prepared to test on the gate issue, Eager suggested Jovial do more with his inside leg. He explained how important it would be for Jovial's horse if he could think about getting the horse's attention away from the gate. One way he could do this would be doing more with his inside leg and hand. The main thing he would be doing with his outside leg would be using it to block the life. He could then use the inside leg a little further back, to push the hind quarters toward the outside. This would help prevent the horse's hindquarters from shoving out the gate. Jovial understood the concepts but he admitted what Eager already knew. At this point in his riding, his legs were just "going along for the ride." So after a little more visiting, it was decided that Eager and Bonita, Jovial and his bay horse, and the Serious One on Thoroughbred would ride out on the trail. They would report back to the others over the prepared meal.

19

When Eager, Serious, and Jovial left to ride the trail, everyone else unsaddled and adjourned to the patio area. Man had already started the chicken on the barbeque. Missy would have liked to go along, but she needed this time to help with the food. Besides, she pretty well knew what would happen on the trail. She knew Eager would try to show Jovial how to keep the horse between his arms and legs just going down the trail. This would help him later with the gate problem. She also knew Eager would try to impress both riders with the fact that their horses had had these undesirable habits for some time. They did not get these habits in a day, and they would not get over them overnight.

The riders would need to ride with more awareness. Sometimes, they would not do anything really different, except be aware of what was happening. Serious was a rider who rode with a lot of life in her body. Jovial did not use his body much at all. In her mind, Missy pictured what Jovial's horse would look like coming back to the barn with Serious riding. Likely, the picture would be an energetic walk. Then if Jovial rode Serious's horse, she doubted if it would even break into that annoying jigging.

Since the session was over, Nana had driven the babysitter home. Boy had joined the group at the patio. Now wearing size two, quite past the baby stage, he was a walking, talking perpetual motion machine. Watching him was pretty entertaining though, as Club Leader put it, almost exhausting. Man and Missy laughed when they told her they had read in a magazine that a well-conditioned athlete would not be able to keep up with a two-year old. They had thought that was quite absurd. So, one evening Man decided to test the theory. Every time Boy stood up, sat down, or turned around, Man did the same thing for half an hour. By the end of that time period, Man was ready for the couch and Boy was still going strong.

The food was ready for the table when the three riders appeared, moving almost as Missy had pictured. When they had ridden in, Serious had returned to the barn along side Eager. Mama used a ground-covering, extended walk that Missy really enjoyed. When Mama had come from Determined's ranch, her walk was one of the many things Missy had noticed with pleasure. Serious's horse was now almost as relaxed as Mama and walking out quite comfortably. Jovial's bay, on the other side of Mama, was keeping up the pace. All three horses looked energetic yet relaxed. Missy hurried to take care of Mama, Eager joined the group at the patio.

Club Leader was the first to question Eager about the change in the two horses. Eager promised to try to explain over dessert. He figured all the riders would be there by then. It would be a more relaxed time. He knew Missy would want to hear the explanation. If he did not wait until she was present, he would have to repeat it all.

After everyone had eaten, Eager took the opportunity to ask Serious and Jovial to explain their ride on the trail.

Jovial spoke first. He talked about riding down the trail trying to keep his horse between his arms and legs and establishing a feeling of staying together with his horse. It had not been easy for him. It was as though he were riding for the first time. It was difficult to stay mentally alert, to recognize even a small portion of what was going on within the horse. He felt he had a better picture of what was happening in the corral with an open gate. As he pictured himself riding in the arena, he could see that when the horse was coming around towards the gate, the horse's body would be somewhat round, but the arc would straighten out as the horse prepared to exit the gate. Jovial said he felt he would likely do more riding on the trail. He would try to be more alert to what was happening. Since there were so many things to be aware of, he asked Missy if her schedule would allow some time for her to coach him. He found this new awareness challenging, but a little overwhelming.

Serious said it really felt great to ride back to the barn in a comfortable, energetic, extended walk. Now that she had experienced this homecoming, she felt more confident that she could, in time, overcome the problem she had been having. One way Eager had asked her to discourage her horse from jigging was by taking the horse in little circles. There was a little spot in the circle when the horse felt like he didn't weigh a thing. At that place she would take the horse toward the barn. If the horse built up energy again and began jigging, she would make a circle in the other direction. Eager encouraged her to try to allow her horse to feel for the soft spot.

Mama would never have known about all the goings on at the potluck had Missy not been sharing the events with Energy by her stall door the next morning.

In the weeks after Eager's visit, Serious seemed to grow more in her understanding of what Eager had offered to each rider. She became something of the horses' advocate. She was able to explain to the other riders how to apply some of the ideas presented by Eager. Missy was overjoyed by the way Serious applied what she had gathered and delighted she could share with the other riders.

Fall slipped into winter and spring came early. Missy was always excited for the spring, her favorite time of the year. Nana loved fall. She always called it her "joy-time." Like many folks of her generation, Nana had been reared in the country. Spring was the season of planting. Summer was a great time and the growing time. A lot of long, hot, hardworking days filled up summer. Fall was the harvest. All the summer's work filled the cellar, the granary, and the barns. All the animals were slick and fat. The work slowed down in time for a person to really enjoy the wonderful fall colors and the crisp clear change in the air. Nana loved fall.

Fall brought an uneasy, queasy feeling deep inside Missy. Every year she fought that feeling, but some years it was more intense. Missy shrugged off her thoughts of fall as she greeted the first warm days of spring. She busied herself planting for summer. Man usually planted a vegetable garden. Missy just planted wherever she found an empty spot. Any unfilled niche she filled with a growing thing. She had fashioned a trellis on the south side of her tack room, both banana squash and nasturtium flourished there.

Boy, now truly two, was with Missy every working minute. She had built him a sheltered, safe play area beside her tack room. He loved to push his trucks and cars in the loose sand there.

This year she had turned the peacock and his two hens loose on the property. The hens had nested and now were followed by their little ones. Missy liked to watch the hens teach their little ones. She was really amazed how much and how soon they expected these tiny balls of fluff to cooperate and complete certain tasks. The day she watched Mother Pea Hen call all to fly up, one board at a time, to roost on top of the fence under her wings, Missy almost missed giving an appointed lesson. Actually, Mother Hen was the lesson.

Teeny, Merry and Nervous all quietly watched with Missy as the five tiny chicks flew up the board fence. Mother perched there and talked each one through its new experience. Each little one seemed to experience the event differently. The first of the five peeped and walked about near the bottom board, but almost immediately seemed to feel an urge to try his little flight. Once he gained the bottom board, it seemed quite simple for that chick to repeat the feat four more times and soon he was snuggled under Mother Hen's wing. The mother's coaxing eventually settled four of her young ones. Three of the chicks conquered the fence ladder almost together. One poor little one could not seem to get up the courage to even try. Those watching held their breath, as the chick seemed to become more distressed. He walked the ground under Mother Hen's fence perch and peeped louder and louder in protest. Missy wondered what the mother would do. The chick seemed too small to make the trip from the ground to the top of the fence.

Actually, however, none of the chicks had gone from the ground to the fence top. Each baby chick had gone to the first rail, then settled for a moment. Gathering courage and strength, each one in turn had advanced to the next higher rail until at last each was safe and steady under Mother Hen's wing. Up on the top rail perched Mother Hen, wings spread wide, sheltering four chicks; far below one tiny fluff ball peeped in loud protest.

Nervous wondered if they should rescue the little one and just raise it by hand since the mother did not seem to have the ability. Teeny thought maybe they should catch the little fellow and place him on the fence near Mother Hen hoping she would then know what to do. Merry wanted to wait at least a little longer. Missy was fascinated watching this mother. She felt there was likely something she would learn that could apply in some way directly to her life. They all waited.

Mother Pea Hen talked to the chick that continued to agonize its plight on the ground. The four protected babies made settle-down-to-sleep sounds. The sunset and light began to fade. The chick on the ground grew quiet, closed its eyes and seemed to be in sort of a trance. Missy wondered, what next. After a slight lull in activity, Mother Hen gave one more urgent-sounding call. Baby chick came to attention with a very loud cheep. In a moment of what seemed desperate determination, the chick raised itself to the bottom fence rail, and then repeated its assent until it was again with Mother Hen.

Missy smiled to herself and Merry. Missy wondered what Teeny and Nervous could have learned. She doubted if they would be so quick again to feel animal problems should all be solved by humans. Missy herself felt humbled, watching all the intricate workings of a Master Plan.

This spring was one with showers just about every afternoon. Each day started clear and bright and the grass grew and grew. All the boarders and students seemed to be enjoying a real period of relaxation. Occasionally, Eager would drop by on his way to or from his bosses' various ranches. He always found time to visit with the riders and encourage and advise whenever he could.

Missy was pleased things were going so smoothly; it gave her time to ride Mama. She was pretty set on showing in the Two-Reined classes this season. She told herself it really would not be a great loss if she did not show, but she did enjoy competing. There would only be a few shows close to home. These were the ones in which she was interested. They were mostly late summer and fall, which gave her more time to prepare. She felt pretty fortunate to be able to use the cattle on the river pasture for her practice stock.

A month went by so filled with normal activities it felt like nothing was happening. Jovial had taken time away form the stables while he had surgery on his knee. He was not back riding but he had been to the stables and hitched up his yellow cart for a drive. It was a pleasant sight to see the man in the little yellow cart enjoying the springtime on the trail.

Boy was in his safe place and Missy was unsaddling Mama when it happened. *So fast.* Boy was *not* in his safe place! He had darted undetected directly in front of the bay horse pulling the little yellow cart. Missy saw him too late to call out, to reach out, and to rescue. Jovial did not see him at all. The trio of Jovial, the horse, and the cart rattled by, missing the little fellow by inches. Missy scooped him up just as they passed. One quick look confirmed he was not even scratched. The next glance revealed how he had escaped from his safe place. Piling up toys had given him a start to climb his fence and go over the wall, so to speak. Missy gave that young man one good swat on his padded backside and placed him inside his safe place. It had all happened so fast she had not had time to think. Then she felt the fear, then relief, and finally the guilt. She felt so frustrated with herself and completely inadequate. She busied herself with barn chores, but stayed near enough to Boy to watch him return to safe play. But nothing took away her sting for administering the swat.

As she mulled this over in her mind, she became aware of a sound coming from the high grass, under the plum tree. Mother Pea Hen had crossed through the tall grass and was on the path calling to her now stranded and frightened chick. Four had followed closely behind, but one little straggler was peeping his fears. Missy was not certain, but she thought this was the bravest chick, the one who had first mastered the fly-up. Of one thing she was sure, he was a really noisy fellow. Mother Hen walked up and back on the path and continued to call the chick. Suddenly, he burst from the grass in a hurry to catch up with Mother Hen. Just as suddenly, Missy got a big surprise. She said afterwards she would not have believed it, if Merry had not seen it too. Expecting Mother Hen to console her chick, Missy and Merry were taken aback when Mother Hen separated the feathers at the tip of her wing and gave that young one a sound whoop and then did it again, over and back. The peacock family left in tight formation with the wayward chick just behind Mother Hen. Old Mama remembered that was the talk of the stables for several days. Missy said she had a lot to learn to become as good a parent as Mother Peacock. To discipline in love seemed natural, to the natural world.

20

Old Mama took time away from her travels into the past for a short nap. The nap was shortened by the buzzing of fall flies. These pests were more bothersome in the fall it seemed than in any other season.

She thought back to the fall she and Missy competed in the Two-Rein. Actually, they only went twice and they got two blue ribbons, but then again the classes were fairly small. Soon a viral infection started in the valley, and Missy chose to stay away from gatherings like fairs and horse shows. Missy did not want to chance bringing any illness home to the stables. Too much was at stake. She finally had her barn full of year-round boarders and lesson horses. They had settled into a routine and she liked that.

One of the high spots for Missy that fall had been an opportunity to meet Wise One. Eager had called one Friday evening to invite Man and Missy to his home on Saturday. He said he was working on some horse projects and Wise One would be there for lunch. They were invited to come share the time and the food. Missy hurriedly called Nana to ask if she could watch Boy. Girl would enjoy watching the horses or she would play with Eager's children.

Missy and Man were so in awe of everything they experienced that day that they never stopped talking about it all winter. Missy couldn't wait to bring Gorgeous in from the pasture where she had been running in the hills and developing agility. She wanted to winter Gorgeous on a really good ration. She was planning to start riding the filly in early spring.

Missy was even more anxious to begin work with Gorgeous after watching Eager's work with the colts under his mentor's guidance.

Missy was extra fussy about Mama's feed that winter, too. She wanted Mama to be in the very best of health with a shiny coat in early spring. Missy was giving riding lessons to a mother and daughter from across town. These lessons were paying for a breeding fee come spring. The new sire was a well-behaved, copper penny colored, fifteen-and-a-half hand stallion. Missy had chosen him partly because of his gentle nature. Being able to exchange work for the breeding was a definite plus. Missy told Mama her blue ribbons in the Two-Rein class had first attracted the stud's owners. The owners wanted their stud to produce some showy offspring. They felt Mama could help.

One of the newer additions at the stable was a round pen Man had built that fall. It was forty-five feet in diameter and filled with sandy footing. It stood waiting for Missy to begin working with Gorgeous. Missy felt that not only were the facilities prepared, but also Gorgeous was ready, and Missy herself felt ready and anxious. During her fall visit at Eager's place, her perception of working with Gorgeous had changed. In the past, working with a horse had begun with a mental picture of how she would teach the horse to do the various moves. Thinking of that now, she realized the absurdity of teaching this magnificent animal how to move out, walk, trot, gallop or run, how to stop, back up or spin around. The horse already knew how to do all of this. What she focused on now was a way to communicate with Gorgeous. She wanted a way to get into the filly's mind.

After years of meeting people who had theories about how to teach the horse, she had met a man who said the horse taught him what he knew. Seeing him that day at Eager's, listening and observing it really seemed the horse had taught him a lot. The amazing part was he gave the horse all the credit. Looking back at her failures and successes, Missy could begin to see how much each horse had had to adjust to her. One of the fellows who had stopped by Eager's spread shook his head in disbelief at what Wise One helped him to see. He took his hat off and scratched his head. Everyone laughed out loud when he said, "All this time I've been thinking I've had my horses handy, but all my horses have learned in life is to get out of my way." That afternoon was definitely a turning point. It was a humbling experience for Missy, for she knew just what that fellow meant. Still there was an intense excitement in beginning this new approach to understanding the horse. Another of Eager's friends who had come to watch confided to Missy, saying "With Wise One's ways, even if you get just a little bit, it will always be there. When you start the horse this way, even if the horse has a different rider, if the horse comes back to you and you offer this, it will be there in the horse."

As Old Mama pictured that time with Missy starting Gorgeous, her mind flashed further back. For just an instant, it was Bonita's first saddling. She and Determined were alone in his round corral. It was a summer evening in the high sage country. She remembered that when he led her to the corral, some young fellows followed. When moments passed without action, the spectators left. These young guys were looking for action, lots of activity and dust. They could not know how hard Bonita was trying to understand and anticipate what Determined expected of her. Determined, for his part, had gone into this starting project determined to find a way they could work it out together. He could not bear the thought of causing her to lose the look deep within her eyes. Hoss had once spoken of looking into her life spirit there. Hoss had had a way of being with her that Determined realized was special. He was anxious to find that feeling. Whatever he tried to introduce her to that day, if she did not do as he hoped, he did not doubt her. He knew she did not understand. He stopped and took a fresh start.

The day Missy took Gorgeous to the round pen for the first time dawned without wind, fog, or clouds. The surrounding peach orchards were in bud. Missy had chosen a day in mid-week with the least possible chance of interruptions. Since this was to be a do-it-yourself project, she had arranged for it to be just that. Mama would get her exercise for the next few days in the outdoor arena or on the hot-walker. Missy could observe either area from the round corral. Mama could watch Missy and Gorgeous either way, too.

Both Mama and Missy knew there was nothing magic about the round corral. A horseman doesn't need a round corral to do for the horse what usually gets done in the round corral. Some riders put too much emphasis on that. There are folks who put the horse in the round corral, then work the horse into a lather, wear him out, and think they are teaching something. In reality, what they have done is build in more problems. They have by-passed the opportunity to allow the animal to lose some of his flight instinct and come to the horseman for friendly support.

Missy had talked to Eager by phone the evening before. He had tried to give her confidence to feel free to experiment. He reminded her to look for the soft look in the eye, a relieved sigh, or a softening in a muscle. He told her to let Gorgeous know when she was doing what Missy wanted. She could tell her with her timing, by easing up as a reward. She could let her know with her very presence, with encouraging pats and rubs.

Missy knew she could introduce Gorgeous to the saddle and bridle without any great fuss or problems. She was already pretty capable around horses. The something different about this was that she wanted to reach Gorgeous on a deeper level. She had seen and felt the connection between Wise One and the horse. It was acted out in the physical area, but the connection was mental and more than mental. One of the gals Missy met at Eager's described the experience as, "A whole different level of awareness and consciousness." It really was a challenge.

When Missy and Gorgeous were alone in the corral, Missy kept the halter on the filly. Missy wanted to check for places Gorgeous might be unsure. Gorgeous had been handled since her foaling time. She had had periodic health checkups from the vet and regular farrier care. She had also run free in the foothill pasture, just being a horse.

Missy was not too surprised to find the filly quite left-sided. That is pretty common in a colt. Likely everyone who approached her, who caught or tended to her needs, used a left-side approach. Missy knew she did not want the filly to start with that handicap. She spent much of that morning's session introducing everything from the right side. When they were finished with their time together, Gorgeous was quite comfortable accepting things from either side. Missy felt good about her progress but sensed some reservations on the filly's part. Missy wanted more of a feeling of acceptance, of connectedness. She settled for what she had, hoping she had built in something to build on for the next day. When she started with Gorgeous the next day, she began again right where she had left off the day before. In some ways she was pleased with the progress. In past years this would have been more than she hoped for in that length of time. Had she never seen the kinship that was possible between a young horse and a human, she would not have felt a loss. She felt she was caught between awareness and learning. It was like crossing a wide, wild river on slippery, stepping-stones. She could not turn back. It was truly exciting and she had definitely left the bank.

After a few days Missy called Eager to try to explain what was happening with Gorgeous. He *got the picture*. Did he ever understand that struggle! About the only thing he could tell her was not to try so hard. She said she had ridden Gorgeous in the round corral and everything went well. She was now working with her in the outside arena. Gorgeous was really going as well as any colt she had ridden before. He knew the *feel* between herself and the horse that she wanted. He could not give her that feel nor could she make it happen.

He told her he could come by for a little while early on Saturday morning if she could arrange the time. If she wanted, he would ride out on another horse with her for Gorgeous's first ride outside the corrals. She was more than grateful. Her do-it-herself project had gotten to that part of the program where help was welcome.

When Eager arrived on Saturday morning, Mama was saddled for him to ride. Missy had Gorgeous ready for the corral, too. It was a chilly morning with a brisk breeze blowing. They rode out. Eager noticed Missy was pretty quiet. Mama had been aware earlier that Missy was not whistling.

Leaving the stables area, Missy was watchful of Gorgeous's attention; Missy had been on other colts that had been surprised by a pheasant fly-up or a rabbit scurrying from underfoot. She tried to keep the filly's attention with her by riding what she called a "snaky trail." She got off the edge of the trail and rode in little winding turns. This kept the colt's mind busy, a very helpful concept with colts. Eager had first made her aware of this the fall he had delivered Mama. It was an idea Wise One had shown him.

So, as not to bore the filly, she would sometimes go in circles one direction then the other. After they had ridden out a ways, Eager noticed Missy looked at her watch. Even though he had a schedule to keep, he seldom consulted his watch. When Missy realized she had been observed clock checking, she sighed. She wondered what it would be like to live the way Determined lived. What would it be like to live where time was measured differently. Still, she was thankful she had a ten o'clock lesson group. These and the other lessons, in part, made it possible for her to have a nice filly like Gorgeous. Missy and Man often laughed about their cash flow. The joke was, it did not flow.

Back from the ride, Eager tried to encourage Missy about her progress with Gorgeous. She was truly one of the nicest, well-started two-year-olds he had seen. He asked about her plans for the filly. She told him she wanted to bring this one along in the snaffle bit. She had never competed in a Snaffle Bit class.

Less than a month later, plans for Gorgeous changed. The stable had a visitor. He was a very successful trainer who owned a large stable up the valley. He came because he knew Missy from the competitions in the Hackamore and Two-Rein classes. He had been impressed with the mare. He knew she had produced a foal or two. He was looking for a young prospect for one of his clients. Trainer arrived in mid-morning, just as Missy finished riding Gorgeous. That is, Missy was aware of him just as she finished with Gorgeous. She was aware of his obvious interest in the filly.

She showed him about the stables. After he did the tour of the place, he was introduced to Mama. He told Missy he was interested in buying Gorgeous. He took out his checkbook and asked Missy to name her price.

Missy needed time to think. She told Trainer she would go into the house to get Gorgeous's registration papers. In the house she hurriedly called Man. Neither of them really wanted to sell Gorgeous. Together, they agreed on a price so generous, they felt sure the filly would not sell.

When Missy returned to the stables, she gave Trainer the papers to inspect. He looked them over and said, "Looks like her dam was out of Nevada—by Trailer." He puffed on his cigar and laughed at his own joke. Missy was a little offended. She was quite pleased to tell him the amount it would take to own Gorgeous, but she raised the price by $500 from what she and Man had agreed on.

Trainer wrote the check. Missy gave him the papers. She loaded his filly in his horse trailer and he drove away. She carefully put the check in a safe place, and then she called the girl who would sometimes babysit the children and watch the stables. She went to Mama's stall. She told Mama they were going to run away from home. After the sitter came, they left for a long ride down by the river.

21

Old Mama nodded off again. Just as she was dozing off, she thought about the abrupt way Gorgeous left the stables. After she left, Missy and Mama spent more time together. Missy stayed somewhat bothered with herself for putting a price on the filly. The check stayed in its safe place. Man did not pressure Missy to deposit the check. Then one day, Nana arrived at the stables during a quiet time when Missy was just unsaddling Mama. Truthfully, Nana planned it that way. She knew full well Missy's schedule. What she came to say would not take long. She had been observing the way Gorgeous's sale had affected Missy's attitude. She was not bothered that Missy felt a loss over the sale; in fact, Nana would have wondered if she had not missed the filly.

What Nana was concerned about was the feeling Missy was "second guessing" her decision to sell. It was as though she was playing the "would-have-should-have" game. Nana knew that was not a healthy way to approach the issue. Almost immediately, she brought up the subject of Gorgeous's sale. She listened to what Missy said. Then when Missy stopped talking, Nana repeated what she had understood Missy to say. Mama was quite fascinated by the conversation. It almost seemed Nana did not have an opinion about the sale. Actually, it was Missy who talked. When the visit was finished, Missy seemed to stand taller. Nana turned the conversation to the children's spring and summer swimming lessons. Nana was always willing to shuttle the children to various activities.

After having talked her way through the problem of the sale, Missy deposited the check in the bank.

Soon after, Man constructed a nice new outside arena available to the boarders and students. In the last months, these riders had become more interested in Hunter-Jumper competitions. Serious and Teeny had gone to a series of play-day events, held the first Saturday of the month across town. Man built the jumps for their new course. Everyone was excited to have this addition.

In the spring, after Gorgeous' sale, Missy made good use of the round pen by helping several other owners get their colts started.

When Mama roused again from her mini-nap, she remembered the day there was a surprise visitor to the stables. Mama had looked up as he entered the stables. She had heard much about him and instinctively she knew him. As he approached, she felt he knew her, too. She had heard Missy, Eager, and so many others talk about him. This was Wise One whose understanding they could not quite understand. As he looked into her eyes, she realized he was indeed unique among humans. With an intelligence way above the average, he was an inside-out person. Almost every grown person she had ever met operated from outside-in. They were careful to use their minds to control their feelings. They were often quite logical and intellectual in their observations. They did not know, or had forgotten, "feeling" information can be the deepest and most reliable truth. Children were usually very inside-out.

Here to greet her was an adult human who had entered his world before the so called "industrial age" had much effect on his life. He had escaped being turned into a machine. He was born to a pioneer family who had provided him with structure, and within the safety of that framework he had been allowed the freedom to explore his world and learn from it. Being born a younger child in a large family gave him the advantage of watching others exploring, experimenting, and experiencing the world.

Mama thought, "How wonderful to meet a human who had been allowed to reach adulthood without having most, if not all, of his feelings frozen." In her observations of humans, Mama had begun to realize one of the reasons for the humans' so-called emotional problems. They could not seem to feel their feelings. They did not use their fear until it became panic. They did not recognize their anger until it was a roaring rage.

It seemed the feelings Mama had observed in children became entombed, buried somewhere deep inside the body of the adult. This had never appeared to Mama to be the natural order. It looked like a painful waste.

Sometimes, somewhere in late adulthood, some folks seemed to break free. They seemed to be able to go from the outside-in and recover their "feeling" beings.

She was excited at the chance to get acquainted with an inside-out person, someone who could share her feeling world. In the next few years she saw Wise One several times. Whenever he was in the area to visit, he would stop in.

The very spring Gorgeous left, Eager and his family moved back onto a ranch near Determined. They had only been moved a few weeks when Eager called to inform Missy and Man that Determined's wife had died. In the period that followed, Missy and Man heard from Eager occasionally by telephone. He said Determined was staying busy. Bonita's first foal was now his ranch stallion. Hoss was fine in his home with his silver business. Determined's children were growing. The girls were in their teens with Busy right behind them. Everyone was adjusting to his or her recent loss.

Mama realized Missy's children were changing everyday. Missy had been given an exceptional pony that had already raised a couple of children. Pony was a perfect companion caretaker for Boy; the two were inseparable. It was quite a picture to see them together and they were together an awful lot. When not riding, Boy would be grooming Pony. After each ride he would take his hoof pick and carefully clean Pony's feet. He brushed Pony's coat and curried the mane and tail. In good weather he took his turn at the wash rack.

Girl had become interested in vaulting. She and several others from the stables were going to another stable to learn and practice. At first Missy had thought about becoming involved with the project. After she and Man talked it over, they realized Girl was at the age to be learning from other teachers. She was now active in 4-H and Girl Scouts.

Old Mama remembered these years as the time she was out on the hillside more. While changes were happening at the stables, she had two new foals. The spring after Gorgeous was sold, both Mama and Missy were delighted with Mama's new foal. It was a copper-colored filly, perfect in every way. Mama was bred back to the same stallion on her foaling heat. Next spring's filly was nearly a duplicate copy of the earlier one.

At the stables, Serious moved on to college to study law. Teeny was talked into selling her faithful little horse and bought a big chestnut Hunter-Jumper. Jovial moved to the city. Merry and her Appy were still at the stables and getting along somewhat better. She often helped give lessons to the very small riders. Energy began to ride and exercise Teeny's big chestnut as Teeny became more interested in other things. They heard from the 4-H Leader often. Whenever they had any special classes or clinics, she usually came and brought some 4-H riders. Brother and Sister were sharing an apartment while going to Cal Poly in San Luis Obispo. Nervous still stabled her gray in the same stall. After the new outdoor arena was built, Nervous spent more time there.

Nana came often to watch Girl and Boy ride. One day she asked Man to see again the master plan. Often Nana was severely bothered by allergies. She couldn't wait for the extension on the arena. She was anxious for the time when the lounge would be built. She could picture herself being able to watch and enjoy the riders in comfort. There would be a glass barrier between herself and the dust. That seemed ideal.

In the same year the outdoor jump course was established, Man had built a large tack room for the boarders. Each rider had a good-sized locker space. "A place for everything and everything in its place," as Merry quoted. It was much easier to keep track of one's own gear that way, and in the progression of things, everyone had a bit more gear to keep track of. The interesting thing about Man's building projects was that, as soon as new space was created, it was filled. Then everyone wondered how they had endured without that very convenience all this time. When the new tack room was finished, the other one was used for the gear reserved for the lesson horses. Missy was amazed at the amount of lessons they were doing. Sometimes Man would be the one in charge of a group of riders. Not all lessons were group lessons, and there were various levels of learners. Missy had some students who preferred private instructions. It seemed the only thing that put a cap on the business growing further was a lack of space, and maybe time.

After Mama's fourth foal was weaned, Missy began to spend a lot of time with Mama again. Boy was in Kindergarten in the mornings. This gave Missy more opportunities to leave the property whenever any chance came to help some rancher work cattle. She loved being able to do regular ranch work on Mama. Mama liked to be working again. It made her think of Determined.

Mama knew Missy felt more relaxed away from the stables. These times were like a mini-holiday for both of them. When Mama first came to the Golden State, she was the first horse Missy had owned with a ranch background. Missy had teasingly told folks, "Mama came to be my tutor in the skills of country." That statement was pretty much a fact. Missy had been raised in the city and even though she had entered and won in Western classes in her teens, these events did not involve cattle.

When Girl was born, Missy had shared a room in the hospital with a young rancher's wife. They had gotten quite close and continued their friendship as their girls grew up.

Missy and her new friend were definitely "town and country," but they had much in common. It was through her country friend that Missy got her first chance to help with cattle work.

After Mama came to the stables, Missy had told Mama about her first time helping gather. Even though Missy had ridden in the foothills many times before, her only mission was to enjoy the ride. When the day arrived to leave Girl with Nana and become a working ranch hand, Missy was so excited she woke hours before dawn. She was at the ranch headquarters before first light. From the main ranch the crew trailered up into the foothills. When they unloaded, Country Friend's father-in-law assigned each rider his position for the gather towards the shipping corrals.

Missy had been assigned a position beside Mr. Pensioner. This fellow had lived and worked on the ranch before Country Friend's family had acquired the property. After they bought the place, he had stayed on. He was still on the payroll but in a seasonal way. In the really foggy winter weather he was more comfortable in southern Arizona.

Missy had been delighted to gather beside this seasoned rider. It was not until years later she discovered it was pretty much ranch policy to pair up the Novice with the Pensioner. It was a policy that could help insure a clean gather and avoid, as the Pensioner said, "A big scatter." The Pensioner could head off any impulsive move the novice might start that would create extra work for the crew.

Missy was excited to ride with an experienced hand. She rode near enough to the Pensioner that he would have her "stay" with the cattle while he would go off through the brush to the left and add another animal to their gather. Later he would point out to her a stray on her right. He would stay with their bunch and ask her to just "fetch-it-along." After she had helped for several seasons, she was told the nonexperienced new hand often served as a handy, human-cow dog during their learning stage.

It was crucial for the cow boss to keep ahead of any possible problem. A rider not savvy enough might even take his part of the gather the wrong direction. It was a common problem for the new helper to lag too far behind or move ahead with little regard to the other riders.

The most annoying novice was the rider who did not stay in position. That rider might see another rider off in the distance seemingly having trouble, and then assume he was needed to rescue the situation. Leaving his section and even his cattle behind, crossing in front of two or three other riders, he would rush to "fix it." What a mess this "weekend warrior" could create!

Now that Missy and Mama were a team, they were good help on anyone's cattle ranch. As Missy would say, "They knew the drill." When the cow boss assigned each rider the position they would be responsible for, Missy and Mama took their responsibility seriously. Actually, Missy thought of it as "respond-ability" not responsibility. Each moment of each cattle drive required each rider to be able to respond to any change in the split second before it happened. This was the difference between the seasoned help and the novice. Missy and Mama were careful to pace their gather so they were not ahead, nor behind, the riders to each side of them. Even in a dreadfully brushy area, they worked for a clean sweep and you would never find them riding in a group of two or three and letting others do all the work. They did their work and were good team players. The bonus for that was they were invited to help with cattle work quite often.

Now Missy had a plan. It was not a new idea. She had for years belonged to a horseman's association that held an annual event. A series of competitions were given throughout the year. Points were accumulated towards a year-end awards presentation. She wanted to campaign Mama and try for the high-point saddle in the Ladies' Bridle class. She knew she would have to work hard. She would have to travel to a lot of competitions.

Missy talked it over with Man, Nana, Boy, and Girl. Missy knew if she reached her goal she would need everyone's help. She could not be on the road competing and giving lessons at the stables and doing everything else. She would have less time for Girl and Boy, although they could go with her some when their own schedules did not conflict. It would cause more work for everyone. Man agreed it was time for Missy to put the extra effort into her goal; he was totally supportive. He felt the exposure she would get by competing would help build their business. He had no doubt she could win the year-end saddle.

Missy and Mama did indeed win the saddle that year. The whole family went to the awards banquet in January. Shortly after the victory banquet, the letter came from the lawyer. Missy was to begin receiving payments from her late father's trust fund.

This would be the year they could complete the master plan. By now the tiny trees and shrubs they had planted were quite large. They had chipped away at the building projects until they had a very nice small setup. Now, they could hire some professional builders to raise up the new covered arena that would extend beyond the existing one. Man would have some help to build the lounge, shower area, snack bar and all the other projects. Their barn would then be able to hold winter schooling shows. They would have facilities enough for associations to rent their barn to hold point shows. All they had worked and planned for was coming true.

Mama felt proud she had been a part of it all since almost the very beginning. Nana teased about the lounge. Finally, she would be sitting on top of the arena fence in comfort. After years of fence sitting in the weather and the dust, she was delighted and anxious to help furnish the lounge. She was in the process of selling her home and planning to move into a smaller place. The big building project was the talk of the stables for months.

The first autumn, fog day came almost without warning. It followed days of beautiful autumn weather. It came on the exact anniversary of the first fall fog years ago. Missy came to Mama's stall early. She could hardly wait for Mama to finish her breakfast. She told Mama they just had to "runaway from home." They rode along the river for hours. Missy wondered how the feeling in the pit of her stomach could be so intense. For gracious sakes, she had a twelve-year-old daughter now!

When the sun cut through the fog, it was a beautiful fall world again. They returned to watch the excitement of the construction. The building was near enough finished by the end of December that they planned a New Year's celebration at the stables.

22

Old Mama remembered well the first spring after the big building project was completed. There was so much more activity, she could hardly watch it all. One of the biggest changes was the crowd almost every weekend. The facilities were being leased to riding clubs and various horsemen's associations for their competitions, fund raisers, and social events.

Missy's students and boarders had mostly been around the stables for several seasons. Through the years, they had shared the same space and often the same information.

Though each rider and every horse stabled there was unique, they had many ideas and attitudes alike. There were several horse trailers of various types owned by the riders who often hauled their horses from the stables to other activities.

One Monday a big discussion at the stables was about the many problems the visiting riders seemed to experience with their horses. The one most noticeable problem everyone was talking about was how many of these folks had a really hard time loading their horses. It had been a lot of years since anyone from the stables had had much of a problem loading any horse. It didn't make much of a difference if it was Missy hauling some colt or Nervous, Merry, Teeny, or Energy hauling their horses. Trailer loading problems were not an issue. Except for Energy and Girl or Boy, almost all could tell a sad tale of a horse loading problem of their own in the past, but in the distant past.

Merry said it made her feel so sorry for the horses and the owners to see such awful problems loading the horses. After yesterday's competition, a young girl about thirteen or fourteen was attempting to load her mare. The pickup was parked out by the solid fence. The horse trailer was a two horse, older, homemade model with a ramp-type tailgate. The girl was handling the mare. It was obvious she loved her horse. Merry had noticed her earlier in the Western Equestrian competition. She felt the girl had a lot going for her. The loading, however, was not going anywhere. The girl would position the mare for the trip up the ramp and just as she would begin the assent, Helping Mother would swoop in with quite a commotion. Her hands and arms would make a flap as if she were taking flight. The mare would fly ahead on an angle and stumble off the loading ramp. After several such attempts, the Big Daddy took control. Helping Mother stood aside while Big Daddy took over from Daughter. If that obstinate horse did not know enough to get into the trailer, he would "By God Show Her Who Was Boss." His hefty yanks and pulls on the halter rope were met with rear-ups and pullbacks. The mare had stumbled over and fallen from the ramp enough by then that her legs were pretty well banged up. Merry said she was at a loss to know what to do. She was not a bit afraid of the horse, but she was just a little afraid of the horse's family. The young girl looked so distressed. Helping Mother was walking in a small circle, sort of rubbing her hands together. Big Daddy was becoming more frustrated by the minute. He caused Merry to want to cover her ears—or wash his mouth out with soap. Merry said she was thinking of going to get help from Missy. Merry truly felt she could have loaded the horse herself, but she was just as sure they would not let her try. Short and sort of round, dressed in pedal pushers and sandals, she did not feel she was the picture of a capable horsewoman.

About then, three more fellows came up. They said they knew just how to load that mare. The mare got a short breather while they found a long rope. Daughter held the lead rope and stroked her horse's neck. She led her horse forward. With the mare headed up the ramp, a rope around her rear and two fellows handling the rope from either side, Daughter tossed the halter rope over the mare's neck and stepped away. That ornery, old nag was propelled into the trailer like a missile from a sling shot. Two burly fellows raised the ramp and banged it closed in one motion. The horse's young owner had a relieved, but troubled expression as she went forward around the trailer. She reached in the small door by the manger and fastened the mare. She rearranged the hay in the manger, wanting somehow to console her friend. What a stressful way to end a fun day.

Nervous had a tale to tell too. She said that following the Saturday event she watched another family leaving. The trailer was a sixteen-foot stock trailer, sturdily built. The horse was fifteen-and-a-half hands, a black horse with one white foot. The trailer door was a solid door. When the would-be-loader led the horse to the trailer, the door swung in, bumping the horse on his side. Frightened, the horse flew back away from the trailer. It was downhill from there. The big fellow who was loading must have begun feeling he was missing his evening meal, even though it looked like he had not missed very many. He had no time to fool with a crazy horse. Loader went inside the trailer and tied the end of the halter rope to one of the slots on the side of the trailer. The horse was waiting at the end of the halter rope outside the trailer door. With a sturdy stock whip in hand, Loader began working at the horse's hind feet and legs with some strikes to the tail-head.

There was no real meaning to the situation. Loader had very poor timing. His main reason for the use of the stock whip was to teach the horse a lesson. It was not a lesson in loading. It was just a *lesson*. Loader got a little too near with the whip and Black kicked the whip away. *What a lesson*! Nervous was relieved when a fellow who knew Loader came along and did the lass rope thing around behind the horse. The horse loaded. Nervous wondered if either the horse or Loader had learned any lesson at all.

Missy had a horse-loading story of a different type. She had been asked by a family for help with its loading problem. She had told them to back their Miley two-horse trailer into the arena. Almost all the other contestants and spectators were gone. Missy felt the footing in the arena would be easier to work on for both herself and the horse. The trailer was a two-horse, but the divider would swing to the side. Missy was careful to arrange everything for the maximum safety and ease of the loading project. She brought the horse toward the trailer, but when she felt the horse's feet stick in the arena footing, she stopped. It was not her goal at this time to load the horse into the trailer. Her goal was to help the horse learn to load, to be comfortable being hauled. While Missy worked with the horse, it seemed like a recorder was playing in the back of her mind, recalling the years of listening and watching as Eager would explain what he had gotten from Wise One. Missy was listening to the horse and how the horse felt about the trailer. At this point the horse was looking at everything but the trailer.

Missy did not plan to make the horse get into the trailer. At this point in the loading, she was careful to watch for any change in the horse that might show he was even thinking about loading. She watched for the slightest change. She watched for an ear that might move a little, an eye to look that way for just a split second, and while she worked, she talked to the owners (and whomever else was listening). As the horse responded to Missy's quiet ways, he approached the trailer and put his head and neck inside. It seemed an "Oh no" feeling grabbed him. Just at that instance, Missy backed him away from the trailer. It appeared to the observers that Missy had just lost that round. In Missy's mind, she felt they were making progress.

Soon, they were back at the "enter position." This time the horse put both front feet inside the trailer and settled. In that second or two, Missy rewarded him by stroking his neck. Then the scary monsters the horse felt were inside the trailer caused him to need to leave. Just before it got too much for him, Missy backed him out, she consoled him, reassured him. When he was ready, they approached the trailer again. To the surprise of the assembly, he went into the trailer like a veteran. He even took a taste of what was in the manger. The folks outside clapped softly. They were ready to close the trailer door, but Missy unloaded the horse. She worked at loading the horse at more of a distance from the trailer. She set things up several different ways. Each time the horse loaded with a comfortable attitude. She did not make the horse do anything. She simply set things up so the horse could find it. Then Missy surprised everyone by asking the horse's owner to come and load her horse. The owner was nearly eleven, petite for her age, but she had watched Missy's loading very intently the whole time. She just walked into the arena, took the halter rope, and loaded her horse. Missy said it made her heart soar.

At Missy's request the little girl backed her horse out again. She led him away from the trailer, lined up another approach, and loaded him again. At this point Missy had her fasten the butt chain and they closed the trailer door. Missy said she had talked to that family since then. Everything was still going fine with their horse projects. Actually, that little girl had made arrangements to bring her horse to the stables on Wednesdays for lessons with Missy.

The group had a big discussion about the importance of letting the horse find the good, soft feel you were trying to offer him.

Nervous said it was easier for her to set the timing up to reward the horse with a soft feel when she was loading a horse. It was more difficult to find her timing when she was riding.

Merry laughingly said maybe they would all get it in another four or five years.

Old Mama remembered the next five years did make a big difference in their understanding of their horses.

Missy grew the most in her understanding, partly because she had the opportunity to ride a lot of different horses. Plus, she gave lessons to many riders. She had the advantage of occasional one-on-one sessions with Eager, who had moved back to the Valley about ninety miles away. Sometimes, she even had an opportunity to visit with Wise One.

Serious moved back to town after graduating from college and joined a local law firm. She had a different horse now. She had given her former horse to a younger rider, a cousin of hers who also boarded at Missy's. Serious still took her riding very seriously. She had come a long ways in her understanding and recognizing the ideas she had learned from Eager and from occasional conversations with Wise One. She read and remembered everything. She was one who could watch anyone and learn something. Sometimes what she learned was the confirmation, "What she had observed was definitely not something she wanted to mimic."

Old Mama thought probably Nervous changed the most during those years. Old Mama felt one of the reasons they had all advanced so much was the help they gave each other. Their feedback sessions, as they referred to them, definitely gave them a home-stables advantage.

With all the visitors coming in and out at the stables, Old Mama had begun to see patterns in the human relationship with the horse. She realized not all riders were as intent on learning from the horse as were the riders at Missy's stables. Part of the reason behind this difference was the fact that J. Q. Public, as Merry said, did not have access to the information they did.

Old Mama had watched and observed. She felt there were different categories of riders. Some riders were very serious about competing, for these riders, their sport was fulfill-ing. It did not seem to matter whether their interest was West-ern or English. There were a few riders Old Mama had set apart in her mind; for them, riding seemed to be an art form, a total commitment. Some were riding for recreation, strictly to be away from their work and worries. She had a chance to get to know those riders' horses. She felt those horses were champions in their own right. They were of every breed and type. A lovable lot, they were likely the majority of horses being ridden in the country these days. They mostly were on good feed, living in good housing, getting enough exercise and regular vet and farrier care. Their humans were loving and cared for them. They, in turn, were taking good care of their humans. For the most part, it did not seem too bad of an arrangement. Some of them were quite proud of their work and some a bit arrogant. Most of them surely seemed to have a comfortable life, job security, and a pension plan.

23

Old Mama woke from her dozing. She realized her right hind leg felt stiff and numb. Anyway, she could use a drink of water. She enjoyed the nice automatic waterers most of the stalls had. She thought back to the time when they used buckets. In the late summer and fall, those awful flies would come to share your drink, then fall in and drown. Girl said that was yucky. Boy used to call it fly soup. These days, Old Mama really appreciated nice, clean water. Old Brown Lesson Horse did not appreciate clean water. He played with his automatic waterer. He played with it so much he made a muddy mess. He broke his nice waterer, so now he had a bucket.

Old Mama recalled that going for a drink of water years ago was what changed her world in the beginning. She didn't take much time to think about that. After her drink, she returned to her warm place in the sun. She returned to revisiting past times.

Once the dreamed-of, new barn was finished, there were more boarders. There were more varied interests. Each rider was pretty dedicated to his or her own special interest. Some of the riders read *Dressage* by Henry Wynmalen.

Other riders never missed an edition of the *Rodeo Sports News*. There was a lady who rode an Anglo-Arab. Her goal in life was to win the "Tevis Cup." Down in the end stall was a big bay that had actually come from England.

Old Mama remembered feeling quite intrigued with all the things horses could do with their riders. The diversity of activities was exciting to watch. The types and sizes of horses and their owners were truly fascinating. It was all interesting and fun to observe from the safety of her special stall and turnout area.

Some of the fun left the barn when the various riders began to get "clique-picky." Clique picky was a term Girl used to describe the behavior of the junior high girls. The distressing part about it was that the term truly fit the antics of the riders even though most of them were far past the junior high age.

The "one-ups" stuff started with a rider who had moved from near the city where her former barn had no Western riders. Mama could not understand that rider's attitude. For most of Mama's early time here at the barn, she had dressed out in Western tack. But the last several years, Girl had ridden her in English attire. She had collected blue ribbons going both ways. In fact, she rather enjoyed being fitted out and fussed over by Girl. She especially enjoyed Hunter Hack classes. She thought pleasure classes were quite a pleasure. Mama always liked looking good. She could not see much difference in which saddle she wore.

Once the clique-pickies started, it seemed to grow like a fungus in the stables. Old Mama remembered she noticed it long before Missy became aware. Missy was very busy during those years, doing things with Girl and Boy. There were times Missy, Man, Girl and Boy would all be away from the stables. Often the family would be gone to some school or sports event in which the children were involved. Usually Nana would join the family for these occasions.

When Missy did become aware of the undercurrents (undercuts she called them), she was not happy about things. She was at something of a loss to know what to do. She wished Eager lived closer, but he had moved up north again.

Eager's attitude toward horses was pretty basic. While he did recognize each horse as unique, he also observed they all had much in common. No matter how special the ration, it all came out the same.

Old Momma's Story

Old Mama remembered the first division in the barn was the separation between English and Western. Since she had been ridden both ways, she could not see what the fuss was all about. Old Mama knew she could jog for Missy or do the collected trot with Girl. Missy could do extended jog; Girl could do posted trot. It depended which saddle she wore whether Old Mama would canter or lope. All those fancy clothes didn't matter to her, because one way or the other she looked good and felt good pleasing her rider.

Then the riders began to divide the barn along the area of breed. As days went by, it seemed there were Arab owners, Thoroughbred owners, Morgan owners and Quarter Horse owners. There were a few Appaloosa owners, Warm Blood owners and even Mustang owners. Old Mama remembered getting a real hoot out of that snootiness.

It seemed to Mama that the more the riders focused on their differences, the more differences they found. She did admit that horses themselves had a real knack for developing a pecking order in a herd. A flock of chickens had nothing over on them. Missy said these "human creatures" that defined themselves as "thinking beings" could carry the "better than" absurdity to the brink of oblivion. This century's history could prove the truth of that.

One morning while Missy was brushing Mama, Nana came to visit. Nana was concerned about the attitudes the riders were developing. It was even beginning to affect the close connection between Girl and Boy. Nana was very protective of Girl and Boy. She did not want them to bear the burden of biased thinking. Nana truly believed, "All were created equal." For Nana, that meant equally unique, equally wonderful, and equally deserving of love and respect.

While Missy and Nana stood discussing their concerns, Man joined them. Man had been so busy with his real estate business that he had been absent from the barn a lot in the last several months. When he was at the barn, he was busy playing catch-up with maintenance. Actually, he liked the change of pace these fix-it jobs presented. He liked to paint and clean. He liked order and cleanliness. The fact that such discord had descended upon the stables was not a happy thought for him. He had invested much money, time, and energy here on these premises. He could clearly see this prejudiced thinking could create problems.

In moments, the group had exhausted their "worry-time allotment" as Nana called those sessions. Since they did not have a solution, their conversation moved on to other news. The evening before, Missy and Man had talked to Eager by phone. He said Determined's oldest daughter, Bitsy, was now enrolled in vet school. The second one, Bossy, was going to be a teacher. Busy, his son, was involved in almost every sport in high school. Determined had tried to discourage him, but he did seem really interested in rodeo. The more his father talked against following the rodeo life, the more the lad seemed determined. Everyone got a laugh from Determined's remarks passed along by Eager. Eager said Determined could not imagine where that boy got his stubbornness.

While talking to Eager, it sounded as if he might be visiting the state within the next month or two. He had sold a gelding to a rancher about two hundred miles south of their barn. Missy and Man had encouraged him to stop for an overnight. Man had suggested if Eager could spare the time, they would arrange for him to work with some of their boarders and students. He could earn something to pay for his travel.

After the picky, prejudicial stuff started, Old Mama remembered the bright spot as being the spot where Energy was. Regardless of the weather, the sun shone on Energy. Whether Energy rode English or Energy rode Western, Energy rode a happy horse. He could saddle up a grouchy horse, but he would ride away on a happy horse. Energy would join a group in the middle of a gripe session but when he left the group, everyone would be laughing. Missy watched him and thought he must be magic. Magic or not, he made "good medicine" wherever he went. As young as Boy was, he could recognize the difference Energy made. Man and Missy were glad Boy took to following after Energy.

When Man and Missy heard from Eager again, he had a definite plan for coming to visit. Man hurriedly began to set up riders for him to spend time working with. Eager could be there for one afternoon-evening session and again the following forenoon. As soon as the word was out, quite a number of riders signed up to be included. Several in the barn knew Eager from years past but to other riders he was a name they had heard about. Missy and Mama were glad he was coming.

Eager arrived about one-half hour before he was to work with the group. There were sixteen riders registered and ready to explain to him what their horses could and could not do. There were over thirty spectators who had paid a modest fee to be present to observe his techniques. Eager had been working with a few groups now and then and had developed more of a vocabulary to communicate his ideas. He had more ways to express himself now; from the beginning, he had been pretty capable at reading people.

One read of this gathering changed the format. Often he began with an informal relaxed session. Each rider would introduce himself and then each in turn would explain what he wanted to change between himself and his horse. But this time Eager decided not to go there. He was thankful, with all the new facilities and conveniences, there was a great PA system in the barn. He had brought with him a special horse. He snapped the microphone onto his shirt pocket and mounted. From the middle of the arena he could be seen by everyone. With the great PA system, everyone could hear him. Watching him, Man smiled to himself. He sat back and relaxed. He knew this would be an interesting demonstration.

Eager did not waste any time getting right to the point.

He talked about how he felt about the horse. He told those assembled that if the rider was having a problem with the horse, he was quite sure it was not the horse. The rider needed to work on himself, on how he was presenting things to the horse. He talked about the closeness he expected to build between himself and his horse. He told the group the horse he was riding was a registered Quarter Horse, with a lot of Thoroughbred in the family tree. He had owned the colt since it was a yearling. He had owned it longer than he usually owned a horse. He said he usually owned a horse until he could not afford to. Man knew that meant until someone offered him more money than he could turn down, as Eager had a growing family to support. Since he did such an excellent job training horses, he was always able to place them in quality homes.

Eager was riding this sixteen-one hands gelding, using a Capriola Western saddle and a silver Garcia Spade Bit. As he talked, he positioned the gelding and roped the dummy calf from several angles. Always his horse was just where he wanted him. With a nod to Missy, the mechanical cow was presented for Eager and the horse to work. That task finished, Eager put his reins over his saddle horn, crossed his arms, and worked a reining pattern. Whatever they did, he and the horse were in harmony. Everyone was so focused on Eager and his horse, no one realized what was to come next. Energy and Missy were setting up the next event. While all the eyes were elsewhere, they had set up a little jump course. There were only three jumps, but that included an oxer and a 4' 2'' wall. When Missy rode Mama into the arena, dismounted, and quickly began the saddle and bridle exchange, some spectators leaned forward. Eager explained that his eight-year-old gelding had never been jumped. He had never been ridden in an English saddle. Eager's point was that it did not matter. He said, "If you and your horse are together, it really does not matter what tune you're dancing to." Within minutes, he had proved that point. Together, they took the jumps as if they had been doing it for years. The afternoon session was complete with this last demonstration and everyone took a break.

When the riders came back after the break, they were pretty much in a learning frame of mind. The spectators had grown in numbers and everyone was intent on listening. Man and Missy had not enjoyed being around the stables this much in a long time; a positive cooperative atmosphere filled the place.

Old Mama recalled those three sessions with Eager made a turn-around for things at the stables. On the last session, the "Better-Than" rider came in combative form. She was armed with lots of know-how, straight out of D*ressage_*by Wynmalen. She soon discovered that "Sagebrush Buckaroo" had once read the same book. She also discovered his plain, bay horse was capable of the maneuvers and moves her fancy high-dollar horse could perform. She discovered behind his amiable smile, in a fracas of words and wills, he was lethal. Even Missy had winced at their encounter as she hurriedly borrowed the microphone to make a few newly necessary announcements.

In the months that followed, the sun seemed to shine more. Old Mama remembered that fun had come back to the stables.

24

Old Mama did not remember seeing Eager again until he and his family came for Girl's high school graduation. She remembered seeing quite a lot of the bay horse he had demonstrated on during that session. Before Eager left for his home state, "Better Than's" aunt, who had been observing that day, had offered Eager a sizable sum for the horse. Mama had seen him with his new owner and they were doing fine. His new owner was showering him with understanding and attention. He was definitely the type that liked to be fussed over. It was a match.

During Girl's senior year in high school, Nana had helped her buy a horse of her own. Mama had been busy that year having a new foal. She was proud to show off her new baby that spring when Eager's family came. Eager and his family had not traveled far. They had moved again and lived just a few hours away.

Mama's newest foal was another filly. Man and Missy had given her to Girl as a graduation gift. Girl would be attending the local junior college. She would be living at home the next two years. Girl would be the one who was to halter train the new foal. Mama felt almost as much confidence in Girl as she did in Missy. Mama had been around the stables all of Girl's school years. She had watched Girl go off to Brownie's and Girl Scouts. She had gone off to 4-H meetings and brought 4-H meetings to the barn. She had been involved in softball, volleyball, and basketball. For years, Girl had taken piano lessons and swimming lessons. In short, Girl was a pretty regular, active sort of kid. Even though Missy had in her teen years become mostly involved with horses and horse-related activities, she wanted her children to have a broader choice of interests.

In her late teens, Girl had become a candy striper at the local hospital. Mama thought she looked cute dressed that way. Girl had gotten very involved in doing her volunteer work at the hospital. This was now her career interest. She could take all her college work within driving distance of home and everyone thought she would be a fine nurse.

Boy's school years were about as busy as Girl's had been. He had become involved in T-Ball, Little League and Pony League, Cub Scouts and Boy Scouts, and, of course, 4-H, and he took music lessons and swimming lessons too. With the stables in the backyard, there had always been horses. Through all the years of driving the kids to and from this and that, there had always been Nana. Nana had always made the time. If for some reason, Man and Missy were not going to church on Sunday, Girl and Boy went with Nana.

One rainy fall morning, when Boy was only about two, Old Mama remembered Boy and Girl coming to the barn with Missy. Man was out of town on business; Missy was working with a horse with colic. She was waiting for the vet. When Nana drove in, the kids kissed their mom good-bye. Boy took Nana's hand and said, "I'm a doin' to Dod's house." The wonderful "faith of a child" Boy had when he was a tiny fellow stayed with him; it was always a part of Boy.

Old Mama thought about how eventful and interesting it had been to watch Boy and Girl through those growing-up years. The truth was that Missy was not the only one pleased Girl was staying at home to finish college. Missy was glad. Mama was glad. Nana was really glad. Man was secretly very glad. Boy would never have told anyone, but he was happy to have her stay home too. That way, she could be there to help with homework and to support all his activities. She was someone he could talk to about anything, anytime. She was his special sister.

On a spring Saturday at the stables, Nana brought a new edition of a horse magazine. Everyone was excited because there was an article about Eager and how he felt about horses. Nana had already read the magazine and she had brought an extra copy to leave at the stables. There were some pretty good pictures, one taken at Missy's barn. Through the next several years, now and again, there would be features about Eager in newspapers and magazines. The riders at the stables were always interested.

Once, when several riders were standing around Mama's stall talking about a new edition, Nana surprised everyone. What she suggested was that everyone remember Eager often in their prayers. When the group thinned out, Girl questioned her grandmother about her request. Nana said she was pleased about Eager's success; in fact, she was happy for him. What she tried to help Girl realize was that the danger for many individuals was not the hard work and struggle that went into achieving something; the danger was in achieving the goal. While making the climb, people seem to be able to ask for help and to give "thanks" for the blessings they received. Then, oftentimes with the goal in hand, there was a shift in attitude. Nana felt maybe part of the shift was caused by the attention and adoration they received.

Nana herself could get pretty cranked up about new ideas, or ideas presented a newer way, since as far as Nana was concerned, all good ideas come from the "Creator." Nana was not into making idols of the messengers. Everyone loses when that happens. Years before, she had heard Eager refer to the horse industry's "pedestal people" as "Horse Gods." Old Mama remembered Nana could get pretty steamed up about some things.

As Old Mama thought back to the years when Boy was growing up, she realized she had not traveled much. Through the early years, she and Missy had been involved in competitions; in fact some years they had gone quite a lot. On occasions, through the years, she had left her home stables to visit stud barns. The only traveling she was doing while Boy was growing up was usually a short trip; she and Missy would haul out to different ranches to help gather cattle. There she could be a ranch horse again. The only difference was she could not remember any gather being short of help. These were wonderful, relaxed days.

She did not miss the travel. The stables had a lot of activity to keep her mind occupied. Thinking back, that was the biggest change. As Missy's barn grew, so did the whole horse industry. In the early years, there had been a few magazines devoted to horses. Now, there were dozens of publications. It was interesting how often articles appeared now about Eager. Even more interesting was that articles were printed that sounded like Eager, but with other riders' pictures.

That thought caused Old Mama to remember the time the family had gone across the mountains to an event with all mules. It was difficult for Old Mama to picture a show where there were only mules. Missy and Man came back talking about the event. Girl and Boy had had a long weekend without school, so everyone had gone. None of them could quite believe the types and sizes of the competitors. There were races, roping, and stock classes, jumping classes and packing classes. The mules were every size from miniature to mammoth and they did every event.

One story the family brought back was how their attention was drawn to the arena between events, where a demonstration was being presented. They could not believe their ears; the voice on the PA System sounded so much like Eager's they hurried to be where they could see. Not only did it sound like Eager, but some of the phrases were just what they had heard him say. The big surprise when they got to the arena was it was not Eager. It was a stranger on a mule.

Man said, "Why not, that just shows news and views travel fast."

Old Mama thought about Boy and Golden One away at the big competition. When the association first sponsored the contest, they had worked hard to get entries. The classes were not all that big and neither were the crowds. Now, the entries numbered hundreds and the crowds were huge.

Old Mama stopped thinking back, and just went to wondering about her thinking. She wondered if there were a scientific study on memory. It seemed humankind had made a scientific study of almost everything. So why did she seem able to remember her early years so clearly and yet those years when Boy was in high school seemed so vague and distant? One reason may have been that he spent less time at the stables.

Girl used to tease that he had "gone country." He was in high school rodeo. He did his practice for those events away from the stables. Girl was seldom at the stables either, because she had moved across town, to a small apartment near the hospital. She loved nursing and it was a demanding career. Because the stable was still such a busy place and, with no special Boy and Girl to watch, Nana usually visited with Missy at the house. There was someone other than Missy at the stables to answer the phone and the many questions. However, if Missy was there, everyone came to her.

During those years, they did not hear from Eager much. Wise One had moved close, and Missy occasionally took her horse questions and concerns to him, but Old Mama did not remember seeing him much at all.

Old Mama did remember one morning she could hear Missy coming. When Missy was "up in arms" as Nana described it, her red hair bristled and her heels pounded out each step.

Missy had almost infinite tolerance with animals. She had a special patience with children. She could keep her cool with childish adults. But there was another side to Missy. Nana always said when Missy was campaigning a cause, "She could really get steamed up."

Mama knew Missy, and she was not surprised that morning when Missy began grooming her that it was with some very hardy strokes. Missy's irritation that morning was over what she called "carbon-copy thinking." She had had an early morning dead-end conversation with a friend over the phone. It was not surprising the conversation was about horses. Horses were not Missy's life, but they were pretty much her living. She spent much of her day with them and she was quite intent on learning as much as she could about them. She tried to learn from them and felt she was making progress. She thought she had come a long way since meeting Eager.

The rub this morning over the phone had come about because of Eager. Not specifically because of Eager, but because of her friend's remarks about Eager. The friend had taken the stand since Eager spent time with Wise One and had access to visits with him, Eager was like Wise One in his philosophy and actions. This old "carbon-copy thinking" always irritated Missy. She felt pretty sure Eager had learned a lot from Wise One; both he and Wise One had confirmed that. But on the issue of "just like," Missy was inclined to think "like heck."

To Missy's way of thinking, every horse and every rider as totally unique. Her parents had purposely colored her world with that wonder. This was not Missy's first stumble over the thought process that was so different from her own. She had tried in the past to figure out just what an individual would gain from that way of thinking. The best she could come up with was a need to compare for the purpose of playing the "better than" game.

By the time Mama's morning grooming was finished, Missy's mind had moved on to other ideas.

In Old Mama's memories of the years between Girl's high school graduation and Boy's graduation, it seemed time settled into sameness. Life went on, growth and change were happening, but it was like a high desert scene where many little dramas were enacted beneath the grass and sage. Old Mama thought about that, how there were no peaks and valleys during those times. She thought it was probably good that life happened that way. Maybe, without the level times, folks would not mature or appreciate the peak times. The other times, the bad times, might be easier to live through, after folks had some quiet times. With that thought, she let herself drift off to sleep.

She woke with a start a few minutes later. She blinked, fearing she had been asleep a long time, but the sun had hardly changed. This time, she woke remembering her first ranch family and where they were today. All of Determined's children were grown up and married. Bossy and Busy lived near Determined. Bitsy lived a couple of states away. Old Mama had recently heard a story about Bitsy. The story did not surprise her in any way. Thinking about it, she saw the circumstances as a time when life's peaks and the valleys came pretty much at the same time. She thought there were times when bad times brought out the good in people. She spent some time thinking about what she had heard. The two main characters in the drama were two of her favorite people. In her mind she could see them both clearly.

She had only seen Bitsy once as a grown person. She and her rancher husband were in the state because of a big bull and horse sale. They were doing a little sightseeing down the coast and stopped for a short visit. Bitsy had not changed much. Missy had enjoyed showing them around the stables. Bitsy did more listening than she did talking. When she was quite small, her dad had jokingly told her the reason people have two ears and one mouth. The idea had caught her attention. When in a group of people who were talking, she had made a private game of listening twice as much as she talked. When she came to visit Mama's stall, after the barn tour, she told Mama she thought Mama had a cushy life. There was snow and blizzards where she lived.

In the years Mama had been at Missy's, she had seen Hoss several times on his way to some horse event where he would have a booth to display his silver work. She knew he was at the same event now where Boy and Golden One were competing.

Both Bitsy and Hoss were special to Old Mama. They held a heart connection to her and to each other. The story Old Mama had heard about Bitsy had happened last spring. After a routine visit to a cattle ranch, to spay four hundred heifers, Bitsy's plane had been caught in a violent storm on her way home. Her little Cessna had to crash-land in some trees near a big river. The only fortunate fact about the crash was that a fishing party camping near the accident sight observed it. One of the fishermen was a surgeon on vacation from an East Coast big city hospital. Everything was done that could be done at the accident sight, in route to the hospital, and in the trauma center of the hospital. Then the painful waiting had begun. Phone calls were made.

That same afternoon, at work in his shop, Hoss had a strange foreboding. He quickly put up his work and closed his shop. He asked his young cousin to fuel his Buick. He felt a strange urge to prepare to leave. When his cousin asked where he was going, he could only reply, "Where I am needed." Just after dark his phone call came.

Determined was clipping his words when he explained the situation that commercial planes and connections would not put them there until tomorrow afternoon. There were terrible storms raging, and charters were having difficulty with clearance. It was decided they would meet in Elko at the Stockman's Hotel and leave Determined's old pickup there. The Buick was new, fueled, and fast. They would be there at the hospital by mid-morning.

At the hospital at mid-morning, there had been little

change from the evening before. After being given a medical update from Bitsy's husband, Determined went into Bitsy's room. He did not stay long, and then it was Hoss's turn. He thought about when he had made the boast he was a fire, flood, blizzard, and be-there kind-of-guy. He was there for her but he had never felt so helpless. He entered the room and stood beside her bed, as stationary as the many life support systems.

Outside the room Determined and Bitsy's husband watched the clock. Determined thought back to his hospital time with Hoss. All he could explain to Bitsy's husband was, "Hoss has a way!" Somehow years ago, Hoss had connected with Determined through his fog and his pain. Determined and Bitsy's husband waited together. The clock ticked slowly.

When the nurse came out to report a change, she said Bitsy must have been unclear what had happened to her. Bitsy had looked at the large man beside her bed and clearly asked "fire or flood" before drifting out again.

That was a bad time, a valley with a mountain peak. After months in recovery and physical therapy, Bitsy and her husband were at the horse event where Boy and Golden Son were competing. Old Mama was getting impatient for Boy's and Golden Son's return. She switched at flies and shifted her weight and went back to turning memory pages.

25

Old Mama remembered as the seasons changed, so did the pace of life around the stables. Time began to have a different rhythm. Each daylight to dark seemed to move slower, but the changing seasons went by quite rapidly. Boy was in college now. He had chosen to go to the local junior college, as Girl had. He was into the some of the same college sports he had enjoyed in high school. He had not yet decided on a particular career.

Since the stables had changed from the original eighteen stalls and covered arena, the new enclosed arena was like a three-ring circus with something different going on in each one all the time.

Mama liked having her original stall up front by Missy's tack room and when she hung her head out over the double door, she could take in all the goings on in the whole place.

Early afternoon was Mama's time to be involved in the activities. Missy would groom her and she would be fitted out with the smallest saddle in the tack room. Missy gave lessons to some very small riders. Mama loved that part of the day. She knew it was an important job. She realized the importance of letting the little ones get to know and love her. Oh, how she loved the little ones! To spend time with Missy and the little folks was a real joy.

One day, just as the afternoon lessons finished, Nana stopped by to visit. Nana didn't come by the stables much anymore. Usually, she came to the house. That day there was a feeling of urgency in her approach. Once she was standing beside Mama across from Missy, she began to make idle talk, the type of talk used to fill time with a stranger. Missy stopped—stopped grooming, talking, breathing. She wound her fingers in Mama's mane and asked, "Mother, what did the Doctor say?" As Missy let her breath out, she gripped Mama's mane tighter.

Nana used as many of the doctor's words as she could remember. She went from diagnosis to prognosis. She outlined the procedures that would be used, the where and when, the follow-up treatment. Every detail had been thought through and planned before Nana left the doctor's office. Everything was written in Nana's date book. There was even a page for things to do: an "in the event that" list. Missy did not want to look at that list. She carefully put Mama in her stall. She went with Nana to the house to brew tea.

There was a major void at the stables after that. Missy began a frantic effort to find the "right" doctor to get a second and a third opinion. The brief time Missy spent at the stables was like being with only part of a person. Her thoughts and feelings were so enmeshed with Nana's health. She still groomed Mama every day, but the brush strokes were filled with anxiety.

Man spent more time at the stables. He began to give the lessons that Missy usually did. Mama tried to cooperate. She couldn't help wondering, *how*, after all these years, he still plopped the saddle onto her back with a thud. As he moved around her, he never once "asked" or "suggested"; every move was a "demand" or "command." It was an irritation to Mama. How she longed for more time with Missy.

One day, after a particularly trying lesson session, Mama was standing in her stall, back end to the door with her head in a corner, when she thought she could smell Missy coming.

When Missy was going some place other than the stable, she wore a really delightful scent. Missy used to laugh and say that was for going downtown, but mostly she wore "Corral #5," the kind you stepped in.

After Mama readjusted her position to hanging out the open top of the stall, she was surprised to see a stranger. This blonde one had not been to the stables before. Man came quickly across the arena to greet her. Mama sensed that she was not a stranger to him. Man dismissed his teenage lesson early, so he could show Blonde One about the place.

The feature of the enlarged facility Man was most proud of was the visitor's lounge. The lounge was constructed across the north end of the arena and was the height of the arena fence, with storage, bathroom, and showers beneath. It was a great place for parents to view lessons or events behind the large glass front. The spectators were protected from the elements and, with a cooler for summer and a heater for winter, it was a great addition.

When Nana had chosen to sell her large ranch-style home and move into an apartment, she had given them all the lovely old leather pieces from her family room. She had donated everything, from the leather hide-a-bed to the drapes and TV and even the Charlie Russell prints and book for the coffee table. The only piece Man and Missy bought was a small, older frig to hold soft drinks.

Missy liked the lounge, too, but her reason for liking the lounge went beyond the practical and convenience for the guests. Really, Missy loved the lounge. In quiet times, when no one was around, she could pull the drapes and curl up in the big leather chair. There the years slid into reverse with the smell of the fine old leather and the feel of the room, and Daddy seemed so very close.

Man took so much time showing Blonde One the lounge that he was late for his next lesson. Blonde One left with an appointment to bring her nine-year-old boy for lessons.

From that time on Blonde One spent a lot of time at the

stables. She was there for her boy's lessons, she took a few lessons herself, and she came to watch other riders' lessons. She was there during the Schooling Shows. She dropped by to bring Man some fresh baked cinnamon rolls. She came by with an interesting article from a current horse publication. She brought a Charlie Russell print she had found at a garage sale. She had invested quite a lot of money having it framed. Man rearranged some of the other pictures in the lounge to display it in good light.

Man changed some of the stabling arrangements too. It was more convenient for him to stable Mama and some of the other lesson horses on the north end, close to the lounge. Missy didn't say anything about the changes; it was almost as if she didn't notice.

She came every day to the stables to help with the evening feeding and to groom Mama. Sometimes she brought restaurant take-out food to share with Man and Boy in the lounge. Other times, she mentioned the meals she had prepared in the house. Always she seemed to be struggling to keep her pain in check. Nana was sometimes at the house but never at the stables. Missy spent a lot of time at Nana's apartment or taking Nana for treatments. There were occasional short stays in the hospital for Nana. Girl and Boy both rescheduled their activities to be with Nana and to be of help to Missy.

The shortest day of the year and the winter holidays came and went without the usual excitement. The weather set into a dreary pattern of dense fog. Mama couldn't see much of the arena activities from her new stall. She formed the new habit of standing far to the back of her stall with her head in the corner. This irritated Man who had to come into the stall with the halter at lesson time. But at evening feeding time, Mama's precious time with Missy, she was always ready at the door.

old Momma's Story

One morning a rain shower passed over, followed by clearing and the welcome warmth of the winter sun. Mama came out of her corner. She was greeted by another surprise: a visit from Nana and Missy. They moved very slowly, and Nana stopped often to lean against the arena fence and take in all that was happening about the place. She wore a perky purple hat of soft knit. Several little yarn curls were attached to the front, giving the effect of Nana's hair escaping from under the hat. She wore a warm-looking lilac sweater and purple slacks. Nana had never been more than a size seven, but she had always had a commanding presence.

Everyone in the stables came over to greet Nana warmly. Being several sizes smaller and weak beyond words, no one would have thought to approach her with anything but a cheery greeting.

Mama was as glad as anyone to see Nana, to know she was having a good day. While Missy and Nana were visiting by Mama's stall, Girl came. Mama was happy to see all three go off together for lunch.

In just a few days the fog came back. It would be really dense from midnight till noon then it would lift a little and be high fog for the other hours. Some winters had been like that in the past, but this winter it seemed more difficult because of Nana's ill health and Missy being gone so much.

Nana was now often at the house so that Missy could care for her. Sometimes Missy would stay with her at her apartment. Nana's stays at the hospital began to be closer together, too.

Blonde One picked up a routine of coming by the lounge with food things, pizza, chicken, or Chinese. These visits were in the evenings when Missy was at the hospital with Nana. Often Boy would go with Missy or she would meet Girl at the hospital. Man was busy with the lessons or in the lounge with Blonde One.

One evening after feeding, Missy spent time tidying up the lounge. Girl was with Nana that evening. As Missy worked around the lounge, she turned the first month's calendar picture with its snowy scene. She joked about the ground hog seeing his shadow the next day. She thought wistfully about February 14th, her twenty-fifth wedding anniversary.

The next day there was no time for ground hogs or wistful thoughts. Nana had taken a bad turn. She had been admitted to the hospital in the middle of the night. For the next several days, Missy came by the stables only briefly, and never at the same time. The evening feedings were taken over by one of the teenaged riders, which helped her afford riding lessons.

After about five days, things stabilized at the hospital. Missy again spent late afternoons at the stables, but she did not take over any definite chores. It was common knowledge around the stables that Missy needed to be free in case the hospital called.

Mama didn't know if there was anything to the theory of the ground hog's shadow. Mama did not know whether the sun had come out that day or not. She knew, finally, the sun was coming almost every day. On the day of no school, the sun came out early. So did all the children. Everyone came to spend time with his or her horse or a special lesson horse. Some of the young riders weren't even sure why there was no school. Still, they were glad for the past president with the tall hat and beard if his birthday meant a school holiday.

There was a special demonstration on grooming being presented at the arena in mid-morning. Missy had a good friend who had a wonderful way of relating to horses. She had added to that lots of experience and training. She had even gone to school to learn to do what she did so well. Today, she was going to share her knowledge with the young people of the stables.

The demonstration had only just begun when the hospital called. After Missy took the call, she spoke briefly to her good friend and quickly left the stables.

Good Friend shared the serious call with the assembled group of parents and riders. She asked for a silent prayer for Nana and for Missy before she continued with her demonstration.

Since Man had not been at the stables when the call came in, Missy had left him a note asking him to join her and the other family members at the hospital. Boy and Girl had been alerted with one call. Boy had spent overnight with his sister in anticipation of a day up in the mountains in the snow.

By late afternoon Man had not returned to the stables. A check of the lesson board revealed he had canceled today's lessons. Good Friend was anxious as to what to do next. One of the young riders' mothers confided she had overheard Man and Blonde One planning a visit to another stable nearer the big city. Blonde One's nine-year-old was having a mini-vacation with his grandparents, and several other lessons had canceled because of family outings and events. Good Friend left for the hospital to be with Missy.

When Blonde One and Man returned to the stables, it was long after feeding time. Everything was quiet, ready for the night. Mama heard them climb the stairs to the lounge. Lights came on and she could hear music. Then the lights dimmed as the drapes were pulled. For a while the music continued, then it stopped. The lights went out! There were other sounds, then total quiet.

Sometime later Mama heard a familiar vehicle arrive. Missy's pickup had a distinctive rattle. Missy came in down by the office and her original tack room. Mama's heart pounded at Missy's approach. Missy's approach told more than words could about Missy's loss. Nana was gone. In her loss and pain, Missy was headed for the lounge and the old leather chair of Daddy's. Mama wanted to stop her, to spare her more pain. She nickered, but her stall was so far away now that Missy didn't hear.

Missy quickly went up the stairs, turned the key in the lock, opened the door and switched on the light. Mama heard Missy's, "Oh My God!" and then the lights went off. Missy fled down the stairs, out of the stables. Her pickup sped away into the darkness.

26

Old Mama took a break from flicking through her memory book to flick pesky flies. She had spent her entire life being very cared about and cared for, and at this age in her life, small inconveniences annoyed her. Flies annoyed her. Late meals annoyed her. When she traveled around the arena, carrying her small passengers and Big Old Brown passed her up and cut in front of her, that really annoyed her. Just a few days ago when that happened, she had even pinned her ears back and glared at him. She knew he knew better than to show such disrespect for her. Big Old Brown needed put in his place but she did not want to cause Missy any worry. Missy had never been the same since the night of her great loss and the betrayal. What a long night that had been.

Missy's pickup had rattled in again when the stables were the quietest; outside the fog was dense. Missy didn't go to the lounge but went instead towards the girls' bathroom and shower area. The principal people involved in the stables kept some clothes changes in a small dressing room there. After being caught in a rainstorm or other unpredicted event, a person could shower and change there.

After a few minutes Mama heard the shower running and running and running. She just couldn't imagine how Missy could feel that soiled.

When Missy did come to Mama's stall, it was first light and getting near feeding time. She came in with a brush in hand, took off the blanket Mama wore at night, and began to mechanically brush Mama's night away. Suddenly Missy doubled up as if in pain and found the closest corner of the stall. Mama thought Missy's insides were turning outside as she retched. Mama nuzzled Missy's side to try to comfort her, but Missy didn't respond.

Mama was so relieved to hear someone coming, from the sound of his walk and the smell of his aftershave she knew real help was at hand. Then he was at the stall door, this Boy who had turned "young man" overnight. In his haste he left the stall door open. He was across the space in three long-legged strides. He gathered his mother to him and held her tight, in his best bear hug squeeze.

Boy didn't know what she had experienced in the night and she would never tell him. Still, somehow, he did know. He had known for sometime what was happening. Even the youngest teenage lesson students were giggling about it. He wondered about the absurdity of couples having a cheating affair, and about why they always seemed to feel everything was concealed and in secret, when the reality was, everyone knew. They were always so apparent. This failing to recognize the transparency of the affair was probably part of their want-ing to deny the truth to themselves. Possibly, they would have made less selfish choices if they had to face the truth that their unfaithfulness was a terrible type of cheating. Boy didn't really know about love affairs, or cheating affairs, as he thought of them. Heck, he had not even been shaving that long. But he had grown up knowing about cheating and lying and such from his years in church with Nana. He knew if you stopped yourself before you started some stuff you knew you shouldn't do, it was a whole lot easier than mucking your way out later.

Boy felt his mother's body trembling in his arms. He wished she would cry but he knew she wouldn't. He had never seen her cry, so he just held her tighter. Instead, hot tears stung his eyes and slipped down his face. He wanted Nana. He wanted his daddy. In that moment both felt very lost to him.

Daylight was entering the stables and with it came Girl.

She showed the signs of her sleepless night. She had wept and mourned Nana's death, as Nana would have wanted. In her hands she carried Nana's date-book planner, with all the pertinent information Nana had given her. On this day, she was prepared to do what Nana had wanted.

Her heart ached when she entered Mama's stall. She saw her mother crumpled in her brother's arms. Her six-foot-two brother looked at her with the hurt-filled eyes of a three-year-old. Girl was thankful she had taken time to call her prayer group. She patted Mama's nose as she crossed to the ones she loved. Today, she could be mother to her mother, and she would parent her brother if he needed.

Old Mama remembered how all three gathered around her and finished her morning grooming. Slowly, Missy's hands lost their trembling. Soon, they began to discuss the notes from Nana and to organize the needs of this day. Girl took the lead role and Missy and Boy rallied to support her.

The Good Friend, who had been at the stables the day before, joined the three as they left Mama's stall. Girl was glad to see Good Friend. These four were so busy talking they didn't hear Man's car park near the back entry, but Mama heard him enter. He was on the edge of the group before they became aware of him. As Missy's hand flew to her stomach and she visibly retreated, it confirmed for Girl what she feared had indeed happened. Girl was glad for Good Friend's support of her Mother, as they quickly left to take care of their Nana list. Girl sensed Boy would like to bolt, too. She quickly assigned him to meet incoming relatives at the airport. Girl and Man were left alone. She would have liked a shoulder to cry on, but this was out of reach for her now. She read Nana's requests out loud to Man. His name was on Nana's list. He had lots of things to do. Girl looked at the list. She looked hard at her father. Yes, he certainly had lots to do and she thought, "He just better damned well get to them." They left the stables together.

Evening chore time brought Missy and Good Friend back to Mama's stall. For now, Mama's needs were all the chores Missy was accountable for at the stable. Mama was always anxious to see Missy. Often Missy talked to Mama as she brushed and cared for her. She could tell much about Missy's feelings by the way she moved about her. She was glad that evening that Missy had Good Friend to talk with. It was decided Good Friend would spend the night. Missy said she didn't feel much like sleeping, and would Good Friend mind using the queen-sized bed in the master bedroom; she knew if she slept at all, it would not be there.

Before they left Mama's stall, they made a plan to move all of Missy's belongings to the guest room downstairs. Before Girl left home, it had been her room. It had a sunny, bay window facing the east, where one could enjoy the beautiful first light of the sun coming up. Good Friend said she would go to the corner market for the items the refrigerator lacked. With a determined set to her chin, Missy asked her friend to bring back a box suitably sized to hold all her nightclothes and personal apparel. This box would go into the garage for storage, until she could find a place to give it all away (or burn it). She would sleep in her sweats tonight.

Good Friend knew something of what her friend was experiencing. Twenty years before she had gone through a similar situation. Earlier in the day, she had been with Missy when she made the candid call to her family doctor. Good Friend would go with Missy to the doctor's office when the office opened in the morning. Missy had eaten very little all day. What she had eaten, she had lost soon. Good Friend hoped the doctor would be able to help with that problem, too.

The second morning after Nana's death, Mama noticed a quiet numbness about everyone who came and went. Basically, everyone was keeping their usual routine as they moved about their duties in a trancelike state. She saw very little of

Missy and Good Friend until evening. They had had a very busy day, which included a trip to the doctor, then to the drug store on the corner. By the time they came for the evening feeding, Missy had begun taking the tiny pills. These tiny pills pushed her pain away. They created a space where Missy could retreat and push everything away. Everyone marveled at her composure through the funeral and the days that followed. She packed Man's things and put them in an orderly fashion on the porch for him to pick up or, as she told Good Friend, the garbage collector, whichever came first.

Good Friend stayed and helped Missy through this period. She got into Missy's habit of telling Mama her concerns about Missy, or whatever else was bothering her. Missy's dependence on the tiny pills bothered her. She worried that the pills were keeping Missy's feelings so in check she was heading for real trouble. Buried feelings can create a tomb of one's life. When Good Friend's own business matters became urgent, she left Missy, but not without some misgivings. The evening before she left, she lingered in Mama's stall, trying to weigh her need to go against her feelings of concern for her friend. It wasn't that Missy hardly slept, ate little, and seldom, if ever, smiled. There was a deepening depression. It seemed to Good Friend that an unseen weight was crushing Missy.

An uneventful period followed Good Friend's leaving. Missy was busy putting things in order. She cleaned every closet, crook and cranny in the house, the garage and the stables. There were trips to Girl's apartment, to Good Will, and to the dump. She worked on her projects as one obsessed.

With his dad and Nana gone and his Mother so obsessed with her cleaning and organizing, Boy spent more and more time at Girl's apartment across town. With Nana and Man gone and Boy so often at Girl's apartment, Missy felt more and more empty and alone. For some time she would tell Mama how she felt—then Mama noticed she became quieter and quieter when she came to feed and groom. She never even whistled one little note.

Then one Friday in early spring, she came and took Mama from her stall. Other spring days in years past, Missy had done what she called, "run away from home," to enjoy a solitary ride in the country. This morning was different. Missy was completely quiet as she selected the tack. From back in the corner, she retrieved the oldest, most worn saddle she owned. She selected the rest of the gear to match. Mama was used to dressing proud. She would have been insulted, except the strangeness of it all upset her. Outside the old, open, one horse-trailer was hitched to the old feeder pickup. When Missy loaded Mama, Mama wondered what sort of trip was planned. They were definitely bound for the hills, pavement to narrower pavement, then gravel, then through a gate Missy unlocked onto a rutted dirt road, rough and rocky. Mama began to feel Missy was making a mistake. The ride was rough and dirty and overhead clouds were rolling together. This was not fun.

Mama was relieved when Missy finally pulled off the rutted road into a small grassy meadow. She unloaded Mama and reset the saddle. With Missy in the saddle directing their way up the gentle slope, Mama felt more at ease then she had all day. Down an incline into a spring-fed creek, a blaze of early poppies greeted them, causing Mama's heart to rise a bit more.

After crossing the creek, the land began to stand up. The climb caused Mama to concentrate on how and where she placed her feet. It was not that the ground was rough, but the winter moisture still deep within caused the ground to be soft. The footing was unpredictable. Still they climbed and Mama's tired muscles began to ache. Sometimes it seemed they were on a trail, but then they were making their own trail, yet Missy kept pushing. They were doing okay until it began to rain. It started with a little sprinkle of light stuff, but before Mama had gone another forty feet, it became a drenching.

The soft sidehill quickly became a slippery bog. Mama recalled from her past every move up the mountain, following the wild bunch across the loose shale, her very first spring. She felt again the spring flood in the wild river water carrying Determined and the calf. Her instincts guided each step. Her will carried them forward. Just when it seemed they were to reach the top and be on firmer, level ground, the hillside slipped away beneath her feet. As the earth moved, Missy stepped from the saddle, onto the hillside above Mama.

It was over in a moment. A clump of brush and rocks had stopped the slide. Mama was a muddy mess. As the sloppy earth had moved under her, it had taken her feet and left her scooting along on her side. In seconds, Missy was at her head, urging her to stand, to ease forward onto firm ground. This was the Missy Mama knew and trusted. Together, they moved to safety. As they rested from the ordeal, the rain stopped and the sun shone, as only it can just after a rain.

Mama's body trembled from the stress. As the tremors continued, she realized that the fall had done more than cover her with mud and grime. Something was not right. As she attempted to position her weight evenly on all quarters, pain radiated upward from her right stifle. As Mama became aware of her injury, so did Missy. It would be a long and painful trek back down the mountain, across the creek, and up the hill to the trailer.

When they finally reached the creek, Missy gently stroked Mama's neck and waited for her to rest and drink. While they stood there on the bank, Missy reached into her jacket pocket for a full bottle of tiny pills. She took the cap off the bottle and sprinkled them all into the fast-moving water. Mama was relieved they were gone.

It was late afternoon when they reached home. Mama was glad this day was about over. Missy pulled the trailer near the back entry, which was handy to the wash rack and the shortest distance to Mama's stall. On the drive from the hills,

Missy had formulated her plans, as to what and in which order she could best care for Mama. Missy knew this trip into the hills and back would be a turning point forever in her life and in Mama's.

After Mama was washed off and rubbed down, Missy began to assess the injury she had caused. Although Missy had never had a formal veterinarian class, she had had over twenty years of dealing with the various injuries that occur around a stable. After washing Mama, she stood her in good light, on a level surface. Standing, the injury was not obvious. From their experience in the hills, Missy felt Mama had sustained a supporting leg lameness. Although she dreaded confirming her suspicion, Missy realized she needed to know.

While Mama stood patiently, Missy performed the various, more or less standard, steps for determining the extent of the injury. Next Missy implored a passing student to lead Mama away from her toward Mama's stall. As Missy followed Mama, she could plainly see Mama's weight seemed to sink onto her left hind. She could see Mama's head lower when the weight moved to the right. The hipbone on the right seemed to rise higher when Mama used that side. Missy's heart dropped, but still she moved ahead with the routine she knew.

With Mama in her stall, fed and blanketed, Missy went to her office and called Doctor John. His clinic was just down the road. She knew he would stop by on his way home. Missy had run cold water on Mama's injury in the wash rack, but in her mind, ice was the answer. Ice was the answer to almost any injury for the first twenty-four to forty-eight hours. She had the ice pack in place when the vet came. After Doctor John ran through his checklist and listened to what Missy had to say, he told Missy he wanted to do a synovial fluid analysis. After he collected his sample, he injected a local anesthetic into the stifle. As he examined and observed Mama after the injection, he was pretty sure about the problem. Doctor John was sorry to realize Mama had this problem, but he felt he could help Missy give her care. This type of injury could be crippling to a racehorse or a performance animal. A horse used lightly, as a children's horse or even a broodmare could, in time, comfortably continue its normal activities.

There were things Missy could do to help Mama feel more comfortable. Doctor John made a list to leave with Missy, knowing she would follow the list to the letter. He also knew he would be asking her to find a nice small pasture to turn Mama loose. It would be better to allow her to exercise and move freely at her own pace.

27

Missy chose to turn Mama into a little, grassy pasture right on the property. She reasoned Mama might need extra care. The other side of that truth was that Missy needed Mama. Part of Missy's mind wanted to do the guilt thing. It tried to do "if only" and "woulda'-shoulda'" stuff, but she just pushed a reject button in her brain. She had to move on. Seeing Mama get better was part of moving on.

Dealing with Man, with the formal separating of properties, was part of moving on. It was a difficult, painful process. It was part of what she had been running away from, but she could run no more.

One of Man's suggestions for settling was that he borrow money and buy her out. The house she had helped build, board by board, would be another woman's home. She told him she doubted it would be worth much, after the fire. They renegotiated. Missy bought Man out. With the money coming to Missy from Nana's estate, Missy told Mama, she only had to borrow an amount she would be paying on into the next century. Still, she was moving on.

On a visit to the stables during the property negotiations, Man came to rub Mama's head. He talked aloud to Mama. He told Mama he was sure she would not understand what had happened. He did not understand it himself. The night his world changed, when he left the lounge, he had passed out of the stables by the office entrance. He found the note Missy had left earlier in the day. He knew then how badly he had failed to live up to Missy's needs and expectations. He knew he had lost Nana and Missy and himself. He was not the man he thought he was. It was a bitter awakening. Mama never saw Man again.

The stables were as busy as ever, maybe even busier. Missy even had a stallion stabled there temporarily. He was only there for a few days, while his owner was in the process of moving out of state. Missy had never wanted the responsibility of a stallion, but he was a gentle, quiet type.

One Saturday night, Missy and Boy left for an overnight. They were meeting Girl and her new friend at a horse event upstate. When the feeder came in the morning, he discovered the gate to Mama's pasture was not fastened properly. He discovered the broken latch on the stud stall. He found the stud in Mama's pasture, grazing quietly. He was very relieved neither one was cut; in fact, there were no injuries anywhere. He caught the stallion, led him back to his quarters and repaired the latch.

When he saw Missy on Monday morning, he mentioned the stallion had gotten out. He explained he had put the horse away and repaired the latch but in his nervousness he did not mention where he had found the stud. Missy was relieved to find only a latch was broken. She was glad when the stud's owner came for him mid-week.

Missy was busier than she could remember ever being. She was thankful to be going to get some help. When she had left for the overnight to the horse show upstate, she had a chance visit with Sister. The daughter of 4-H Leader was all grown up now. She was married and the mother of three school-age children. After living on the coast for a number of years, she had moved back to the Valley. She and her husband had invested in her parents' business. The bottom line was that she was looking for a flexible work arrangement, some job that fit around her already busy schedule. Missy was delighted Sister could join the crew at the barn. She had a kind, steady way about her and a better than average ability with both horses and people.

Merry was still part of the crew. She had taken over much of the day-to-day paper work. A few years after the big building projects had been finished, a new structure was attached. The office was small but very efficient, with a lot of windows. This was Merry's domain now. Missy had never cared much for the paperwork end of the business. Man had always held that post, but even before Man left, Merry had been helping out in the office.

Missy was able to share many of the responsibilities that were previously hers with Sister. Sister gave some of the one-on-one, private lessons and she gave group lessons for some of the more advanced riders. She rode some of the colts Missy had in training and exercised some horses that needed extra time spent with them. Tuesday and Thursday, Sister was there in the evenings. Monday and Wednesday, she came in the forenoon. Whenever she came, she was a lift to Missy.

Old Mama thought back to that fall day Missy finally came to visit her with a halter in her hand. As far as Mama could tell, her spring injury was a past event. There may have been a little something there, but Mama knew there was a little something else, something else that was far more important than any silly injury. Even though she had spent the past six months running loose in the pasture, she had still been within Missy's sight. Missy had given her every care. Everyone at the stable had constantly come to visit. They all said how well she looked.

It was early in the morning when Missy caught her. They went directly to the barn area. Sister was already there saddling a tall, rangy, brown colt. After Missy groomed Mama, she set the saddle. She had not used that saddle since last spring. It was the saddle Mama had won for her. Missy let the cinch out to fit and remarked to Sister how well Mama was doing.

This was to be a ride down along the river. Missy wanted to acquaint Sister with that private domain. The river pasture owner had gotten up in years and for several years now, he had leased the field to Missy. She had used the pasture for so many years, she almost felt she owned it. She knew, at least, that beautiful place owned her. She always felt more at peace after a ride there. She had been using the pasture for the mares and foals. Through the years she had kept enough of Mama's filly colts that she had quite a bunch to care for. Actually, she confided to Sister, Mama's get had helped keep things running in those early years. The foals that came now always had a market. She still kept in touch with Determined. He had pretty much built his horse band around the blood of Mama's first foal. Leaving the stable, Sister and Missy were still discussing Mama's grown sons and daughters.

One of the qualities all of Mama's foals shared was her energetic walk. She traveled so free and easy, with her feet right under her. She was definitely a smooth-moving animal. Sister said no one could use "smooth-moving" to describe Rangy Brown's walk. Every time he put a foot down, it went ker-plunk. He seemed to be traveling one step at a time. He was keeping up with Mama but Rangy was rough.

Missy told Sister it had been just such a horse years ago that had helped her find the horse's feet. On just such a ride to the river, Eager had helped her become more aware of the horse's feet. Eager said, he too, had ridden for many years before Wise One had made him aware of really getting to the feet. It had been something of a struggle to learn. Missy thought many riders only feel the foot when it touches the ground. Sister laughingly said she could definitely feel Rangy's foot strike the ground. The way he moved one foot at a time, he had sort of a stutter between steps.

Missy asked Sister if she could feel Rangy's foot leave the ground. She answered negatively. It seemed an opportune time to work on that. Missy suggested they trade horses for a while. She felt the two horses were so different, maybe the horses could help Sister. When Sister rode Mama, she said all she felt was relief.

When they traded mounts again, Sister began to be aware when Rangy was about to ker-plunk a foot. She concentrated on his front right foot. Since they were in the middle of the meadow, Sister felt safe closing her eyes. She thought maybe closing her eyes, feeling for only the one front foot, she could begin to recognize its liftoff.

Missy sat quietly on Mama. Once in a while, she would try to help by saying "there," just before the foot left the ground. Finally something began to click for Sister. At first, she had only felt the foot when it hit the ground; finally, she began to know when it was coming up. Before they left the meadow, Sister could feel the foot just before it left the ground.

Missy remarked of the many times Eager had reminded her, "The time to direct the foot is when it is leaving the ground."

Missy told Sister it is pretty difficult to move a foot that a 1200-pound horse is standing upon. Sister laughed at the picture. Sister was something of an artist, a cartoonist really. It was easy for her to picture a cartoon depicting just such a problem.

For the next few weeks, Sister made it a practice to come early one day a week. She and Missy would ride the river pasture. This time was sort of a mutual benefit time for them; each different horse Sister learned from helped Missy, and Sister was doing a good job with the horses. It made one less job for Missy.

Mama liked this arrangement. She was the one who got to go along to the river pasture. The exercise was just what she needed. In the river pasture were some of her daughters, their daughters, and even their daughters. They would all be foaling early in the spring. Mama was pleased with all of them. Most of their last year's foals had been sold as weanlings to help pay Missy's mortgage but three young fellows had been kept. They now resided in the little pasture Mama had called home all summer. Missy and Sister were spending time each day with them. They referred to them collectively as "The Colts."

Old Mama remembered that fall as a happy time for her. Missy was still not the same Missy, but there were changes toward the better. Missy was awfully busy, but the times between busy seemed to be quiet, sad times. Still the secret Mama was carrying made Mama's heart glad. She was surprised Missy, who knew her so well, had not guessed her secret. Since that time long ago when Mama had come to Missy's as a mare in foal, Missy had always fussed over the event. Each new foal was always planned for and worried over. Mama knew it had not been Missy's plan for her to have any more foals at this late date.

Every day Mama did her routine around the stables in quiet contentment. She had become a lesson horse for really young riders. She liked her job. She liked the children. Mostly, Merry worked with that group. Sometimes, Boy took over that time slot, or Sister or Missy.

One day when the responsibilities fell to Missy, she saddled the three other horses she would use. Last, she saddled Mama.

Old Mama remembered it was quiet around the stables that afternoon. Missy seemed to have some extra time. She had time to talk with Merry, who came by on her way to the office. Missy had a puzzled look as she lengthened the cinch and she told Merry, "If I didn't know better, I would think Mama was with foal again."

Just then the first little rider arrived. Missy loved all the lesson children. She really didn't have a favorite. She used to say if she did have a favorite, likely this little fellow would be the one. He was so bright. He fairly bubbled over with excitement. He seemed to be excited over every new discovery and he seemed to discover something new at least every two seconds.

One of Missy's sharing stories about Little Fellow had happened earlier in the fall. One early evening, Missy had been at the home of Little Fellow's grandparents. Little Fellow was out in the yard on the swing. Just as Missy was leaving, Little Fellow discovered the rising moon. He rushed to his grandma. He grabbed her hand and pleaded, "Grandma come quick!" His grandma responded to his excitement and rushed outside asking, "What do you see?" Little Fellow could barely contain his excitement and joy as he explained, "I can see the flag on the moon." Missy declared she actually got a lump in her throat when his grandma responded with excitement and joy to match the child's, "Really? Which way is it blowing?"

Missy knew her own reaction would have been to explain the facts, the real reasons why he could not be seeing the flag on the moon, regardless of which way it was blowing. Soon she realized, "Oh dear, why wonder why children loose their wonder!"

Old Mama shifted her weight and slipped to a different memory page. In the months after Man left, Missy had spent much of her time in the stables. Missy had always been caring and attentive to Mama's needs. Old Mama looked back on this period of time as her cleanliness period. Missy nearly wore out Mama's hide with brushing and fussing. Any lull in Missy's routine was filled with fussing over Mama. Mama modeled new blankets, saddle pads, saddles, head gear, tail wraps and leg wraps. Every new product from tack shop, vet supply house, and feed store became something Missy could concentrate and expend her energy on. Her need to stay busy drove her. Missy spent all her time in the stables to avoid the house.

Old Mama remembered this time as the time Missy heard from Wise One often. Missy and Wise One's history went back over twenty years. In the early years Missy had been so in awe of him she did not connect with his reality. His was the power of the present. He had a solid core. He knew his uniqueness and accepted his identity as the naturalness it was; thus, he was free to be and to connect with the uniqueness in the world around him. His solid core allowed him to directly relate to his physical world. He used to say he couldn't really explain to folks what he felt with the horses. He would say he couldn't explain what he was trying to say: "You have to feel it in your gut—I guess," was his only answer.

Missy came to realize that his response was an okay and maybe even a profound, explanation. Missy read a lot—she read and it stayed in her head. She once told Mama she didn't really know the way out but it was good to know a different reality existed.

She was comforted by Wise One's visits. Missy thought maybe Wise One was pleased to feel a glimmer of recognition of his reality in the folks he helped around the stables. Since his first quiet sessions of being, as he used to call it, "An Equine Counselor," changes had taken place in the world of horses. Many riders were now attempting to interpret his message. Missy had named them "The Salesman," "The Campaigner," "Impressed One," "The Opportunist," "The Advocate," and even "The Impostor." Missy read the magazine articles, bought the books, the audios and videos. Often she heard the exact words and phrases she had heard years ago from Eager and Wise One, but often the words did not fit the picture. She hoped someday the focus would become clearer. In the more than twenty years since she had first met Eager, new people kept appearing in magazines and books, audios and videos. In the effort to grow and propagate, the term "Training" was dropped and "Teaching" gained the forefront—"Learning" was paramount.

Missy wondered if Wise One, watching it all, felt some dismay. In the stampede to promote and sell the gift he had wished to share with the world, it was being trampled under-foot. It was being buried in the soft dirt of the round corral, covered by the dust of learning—and *wisdom was ignored*. See-ing as he did with the power of the present, Wise One might find it difficult to understand these clinicians who need to dissect the past. Their statements in the absolute about the past were astounding and at the very core, irrelevant. As they struggled to shed old skin and appear all new, the metamor-phosis was still on the outside, still surface and superficial. Horse and man had shared the planet for centuries. Wise One might not understand their need to focus so much on the misdeeds of the past and to trumpet so loudly their new appearance for the future. In Wise One's reality, where wholeness existed, there was little need to fragment the world. Who needs categories for Better or Best or Bad or Worse?

Still, some of the young fellows who had come to visit years before were coming back to visit. Missy felt it must give him joy to realize the seeds of understanding planted in their early years were growing towards maturity even as they matured.

On one of Missy's visits with Wise One she mentioned she had seen the one she called "The Advocate" in action. She was pleased with the picture. In the beginning she had wondered about his potential, since he seemed so much a duplicate copy of their mutual friend. She was excited about his growth. Wise One grinned. Missy figured he had known what she recognized. She was pleased she could feel the difference in "The Advocate." Inside growth is something a person cannot fake or make happen—but when it happens, it radiates and can be felt on the outside.

Old Mama remembered it was during her cleanliness period that Missy and Mama were surprised by a visit from Hoss. Missy was in the breezeway—grooming Mama—when Hoss came by. He was on his way back home after being in the southern part of the state with his bit and spur display.

When Missy and Hoss were exchanging stories, Missy told him of the day she had traveled down the Valley in the early 1970s to visit a prominent horse facility. Eager had business there and since she was interested in seeing the setup, she had gone along. The owner had already had much success in the "horse world." However, he was a thinker and open to new ideas.

They arrived early and by mid-morning all the forenoon projects had been completed. They had toured the facilities, seen the two standing studs, been introduced to this year's babies, seen the pasture with the yearlings, and had even seen a long two-year-old's first saddling. During their walkabout, The Thinker had been questioning Eager about the ideas he was getting by being around Wise One.

Thinker had thought early on that it might work out for Eager to be able to work with one of the two-year-olds. Thinker wanted to see how some of this "feel stuff" worked. It was far easier for Eager to explain by doing than it was for him to find words to express what he desperately wanted to share.

Thinker chose a three-year-old filly for Eager's project. This filly was the foal of a Thoroughbred-type grade mare, crossed with a cow-eating Quarter Horse stud. The filly's owner, a rancher in the foothills above Coalinga, had great hopes for her. She wore his brand on her left shoulder. This was the only close contact she had experienced with her owner or any human. This rancher's neighbor had hauled her to Thinker's arena in a little, one-ton truck. She had been gathered from the hillside along with five saddle horses—separated from them in the corral and up the loading chute into the truck. She was stalled by herself now in a small pen behind the round corral.

As Thinker made the necessary gate changes to allow the filly to enter the round corral, he gave Eager this background on the filly, as it had been given to him. Eager always wanted to know the history of the animal before he presented himself to it.

Then they were in the round corral. When the first puff of dust rose from the corral, magic happened. Spectators appeared to circle the outside of the corral. It had always seemed an unwritten rule of the ranch, if there were any action in the round corral, spectators would appear, as if drawn by a magnet to corral dust.

Old Mama remembered that Missy and Hoss were relaxing in the breezeway, near the tack room, as Missy told her story. But, apparently Missy had used up her timeout. She sprang up from the bucket-stool, entered the tack room, and returned in seconds ready to apply a new brand of hoof dressing to Mama's hooves; then she finished her account of Eager's trip to visit Thinker. She talked as she took care of Mama.

As the group of spectators had gathered around the round corral at Thinker's, Eager began getting acquainted with the bald-faced, bay filly. There had been a time in Eager's life when he was uncomfortable working with folks watching. To talk to more than three or four people at a time had been very intimidating for him. It was interesting to Missy to notice as Eager began to get the little filly to *hook on* to him, the spectators seemed quite peripheral to his attention. In his eagerness to share with Thinker, Missy thought his work with Bay Filly was quite the best she had seen him do.

Missy had witnessed the connection he could form with an untamed animal many times, as he helped riders get their colts started. The difference this time seemed to be, he was being more verbal. He talked his way through the entire encounter.

As Bay Filly entered the corral, he began. He spoke quietly to the watchers, counseling them to watch the filly's every move and mood change. He told them to watch the filly's ears and eyes, as they were such good gauges to the filly's feelings. He told the spectators he hadn't always had this approach with horses. In the past he had had the attitude of making the horse do *his thing, his way*. Now he wanted to let the horse do *his thing, the horse's way*.

Eager said lots of people have a picture in their mind of horse training. They are pretty sure things that cause physical pain are things they want to steer clear of; they think of hitting or jerking, chains and restraints, pretty obvious force and fear things.

Eager wanted the gathering to understand when he spoke of *making the horse do his thing his way*, this had not been a physical force and fear thing, rather an attitude of superiority. It was sort of a "Man the Master" approach. Then, he had a horse that did not respond to that approach. This need for a different way had led him to a Wise One.

One of the big differences in his *new approach* to any horse now, was his realization of how very much each horse has to offer the handler if the horse is allowed to use his full potential. Eager said, "I now use his full potential." He added, "I now settle for letting the horse do my thing, his way—whatever way fits him best. I want my idea to become his idea. I let things become his idea." "Let" gives space for both horse and human to express their unique self.

As he talked, he occupied the center of the round pen. The filly moved cautiously around the corral, keeping her distance and looking towards the outside. Only occasionally would she give her attention towards Eager. She preferred to pretend he was not there. Just then Eager kicked some corral dust towards her. Although he did not move from his stance, he moved his presence into her orbit. She startled and lunged forward. He waited an immeasurable instant then shifted his upper body weight towards her. She took that as a cue to hug the corral in a trot. She circled the corral one and a-half rotations, before she allowed herself to slow down and check to see if that fellow was still there. He *was*. He toed another slight dust-puff towards her. She was off again. This time she ignored his presence two full circles.

As Eager watched the filly, he addressed his remarks to Thinker: "You know I've been talking for over forty years, but I have never thought so much about what I was saying until lately. I don't want this filly hugging the corral fence and pretending I'm not here. We can't communicate if she continues to ignore me. A while back when I used to say, 'Make the wrong things difficult and the right things easy,' I realized what I really meant was, not *make* it happen exactly, but more *let* it happen." As he spoke, he moved abruptly towards the filly. Even though it was only a move of inches, his sudden move caused the filly to startle away around the corral. He grinned and observed; "Now that put a kink in her tail, didn't it! That was *make* it happen."

Eager continued to address himself to Thinker: "It's pretty easy for a fellow to get caught up thinking about what the horse is doing, whether the horse is doing something right or wring. It may be the quantum leap in a fellow's thinking to realize the horse is not doing anything wrong. The horse may not be doing what you would like. He might be just too bothered and he is busy saving his life, he thinks. Or, it could be the way that you have presented a situation to him has no meaning yet."

Eager got real serious then and addressed all assembled. He had a way with his gaze, of drilling home a point—he said, "*I can't emphasize this too much. You are not working on the horse; you are working on yourself. You are working on yourself to recognize and realize what the horse is thinking and feeling.*"

"This filly was foaled out in the hills. She had a good Mama and plenty of good feed. She had no knowledge or need of man. She had one trip off the hill pasture to the ranch corral. Considering she was weaned from her mama at that time and branded, she hasn't much reason to want to be my buddy. It is up to me to offer her a reason to want to get to know me, to offer her a way we can communicate. I do have an advantage, because she has hardly been around humans and I've lost track of the horses I've worked with. Since I started this way of presenting myself to the horse, I have not found one horse who did not respond."

As he talked, he moved nearer the perimeter of the corral. His movement caused the filly to change directions. She continued her avoidance strategy in the opposite direction. Eager directed all his attention towards the filly. "I've seen some folks communicate about like this," he grinned, "but we can't have much of a conversation if she is going to ignore me. I'm going to set things up a little different. It won't be so easy for her to ignore me, as I will be doing more. When working like this, sometimes I use something to toss or flick or whatever, to cause it to be more difficult for the horse to ignore me. Since it isn't necessary to use something, I have nothing to use.

"I don't want you folks to be looking for a method—do this, to get that. This is not Do. it is Be. Be aware of even the slightest change in the horse's attitude; be open to her feelings. Be observant of her ears, see how her offside ear, the one next to the corral, is working to take in her surroundings. See her inside ear beginning to slow down its movements. She is beginning to think more about me. She is beginning to prepare to hunt me up."

Missy told Hoss it was so exciting to watch Eager that day. He was so focused on getting the filly to *hook on* as he called it. He wanted those watching to realize what was really happening—to know deep inside themselves the naturalness of what they were seeing. That naturalness of communication and kinship between all living things was not only possible but also attainable. It was available to whomever could turn inside themselves to search.

Eager told the folks, "I can talk to you with words, but I communicate with the horse through feel. I don't always know what I am going to do until I get feedback from the horse. The horse tells me how he feels about the situation.

"Now see the filly, how she is responding to me? Her head is tilted toward the inside of the circle, toward me. Her body is soft from her nose to her tail. She is beginning to work her mouth."

Just then, three new watchers approached the round pen. This diverted the filly's attention, and she startled away again. It bothered the filly. It bothered those assembled even more, so intent were they on watching. It did not bother Eager. He just grinned and said, "It's okay." Actually, it was fine. The slight commotion had created enough fright in the filly that when she finished that rotation of the corral she was ready to *hunt up* her new acquaintance in the center of the corral. This time when she stopped, she lowered her head slightly as she positioned toward him, working her mouth. He was there for her and moved to rub her head and reassure her as he had so many others.

Missy told Hoss it was just moments until Eager had the filly so hooked on that she followed him all around the corral. She had really found a friend. Eager told the spectators, "Every horse can be your friend." Missy said the reaction from those assembled was really interesting. Thinker was pretty intent on learning more. Everyone had an opinion. It was a little difficult for some to grasp the naturalness of what they had seen. Some really seemed to want to analyze from the beginning and build a "how-to process" to explain what they had experienced.

Missy thought the most interesting remark was a statement by the fellow who described what Eager had demonstrated as "interesting" but stated he couldn't see where it had a monetary value. Missy laughed when she told Hoss that the one who had made that observation, over twenty years ago, was now making big bucks selling a similar but inferior product under a slightly different label.

Old Mama remembered how one beautiful fall day followed another. Then, one day it rained. It was a downpour that lasted several hours. The very next morning there was no sun. A dense blanket of fog was everywhere. Missy came to the barn at the usual time. Old Mama remembered how stressed she looked. She had been there only minutes when Sister's little station wagon pulled into her parking space. Missy met her with an exclamation of surprise. She told Sister she need not have taken such a chance with her life, to drive in such awful fog. Sister laughingly replied that she did value her life! She did not purposefully venture out in this fog. In fact, the sun had shone clear and bright at her house before she left. This fog stuff had caught her in a pocket near the river bend. It seemed to increase every yard after that. It really was dangerous out.

No one could have expected Missy's reaction to Sister's explanation about her drive in the fog. Missy's face lost all the color until it seemed her freckles were painted on. Sister was concerned and confused and asked Missy if what she said had somehow upset her. Missy seemed to be almost in another time and place when she asked Sister to repeat what she had just said. In complete puzzlement, Sister told again how it came about for her to drive in the fog. Missy leaned against Mama's stall. She let her breath out very slowly. She told Sister she finally understood. Then she told Sister that for the first time since she was about twelve, she understood how her father's death, that foggy morning, could have happened.

As Missy began to explain her feelings, she was horrified to realize how angry she had been for so many years. For so long, she had pictured her father's driving in the fog as a careless or reckless, deliberate sort of action. Nowhere in her childish mind had she recognized how simple and simply unpredictable a terrible accident like her father's could have happened. Sister listened and listened.

When Sister did begin to talk, she spoke of how children sometimes react to a painful loss. How often they feel so angry that they are not even clear where to direct their anger. This area of human feelings was one of the very areas Sister had majored in at college. Her training placed much emphasis on grief counseling. When she married and began her family, almost right after college, she had chosen to put that career choice aside for a time. She did not feel she could do both careers at once. She had chosen to be a "full-time" Mom, who had some "part-time" job commitments. She knew in the future she would be doing the work she had prepared for at college. That day, she was glad for her training. She was able to help her friend, but truly Missy was more than a friend to Sister; she had become her mentor. Even though Missy was a decade older, Sister had sometimes sensed the wounded child within her. The two women left to go into the house to escape the fog gloom. Nana had referred to such sessions between herself and Missy as, "tea and sympathy."

From that day on into the winter, Old Mama remembered the weather was terrible. But although the weather was bad, Missy seemed to be getting better.

It was not many days after that, while Missy was grooming Mama, she put down the brush and went to have a visit with the chore man—feeder, the very fellow who had fixed the broken latch on the stud-stall last spring. When they finished their conversation, she returned to the barn and immediately called Doctor John. She made arrangements for him to come examine Mama. This appointment was not about a lame leg.

Doctor John came and confirmed what Missy had finally suspected, what Mama already knew. The news raced through the barn. Missy told Sister she was excited, and at the same time quite frightened. She never would have chosen to breed Mama this late in life. She was at a loss as to what and when to tell Determined. He had always been an absolute worry-wart over Bonita's health. In fact, he had fretted when she carried her last foal several years ago.

Missy knew Doctor John remembered Mama's last foaling as being very textbook, the part of the book that explains a normal trouble-free event. Doctor had acknowledged Mama was definitely older now, but he said he had lots of confidence in her and in himself.

Almost from the minute the story got out, everyone began to refer to Mama as "Old Mama." Merry thought maybe she would make the *Guinness Book of Records*. But, Mama had lived on the range with the wild bunch and she knew she was not even close!

Missy could not believe Boy's reaction. This busy college fellow was completely smitten with the idea of the new foal's arrival. He immediately began to read the chapters in the vet book on foaling and the care of the foal, and to ask Doctor John all sorts of questions.

After being surprised by Boy's reaction, Missy began to feel a special sort of joy at his interest in the coming event. He suddenly seemed so much older, more mature, less dependent, more of a partner in the business. Missy realized while she had been moving on with her life—life had been moving on. Mama had never lacked for attention at the stables. Now her condition became the main attraction.

On the practical side, the topic came up about registration papers. Considering the time sequence, Old Mama's registration number should have been included in a stallion report filed earlier in the fall. Since the time had passed for filing the stud report, it would cause more paperwork and likely more of a fee. Missy said she would have to think about that; maybe this foal was too special a gift to fuss with the business side of life.

A couple years ago in a conversation with Eager, Missy had become suspicious of the exact bloodlines of Mama's family tree. It was not something Eager said. It was the abrupt way he stopped talking and changed the subject. Someone in the conversation group had been expounding, with great expertise, about the wild range horse. "Expounding" was Missy's word, and "expertise" was what the speaker seemed to feel about his knowledge. It was very obvious Eager did not share that opinion. He had started to say something about Bonita, then caught himself. Although Missy never brought the subject up to Eager, she was very sure there was some history there. But no matter what he knew, she knew he would never tell.

As far as registration papers were concerned, if they were important enough, that could be an issue after a live foal was on the ground. At this point, the welfare of Old Mama and the coming foal was first priority. Missy did call the owner of the stallion. He was enjoying his new home and his stallion was fine. Owner said he would help her if she decided to pursue registration papers later. She told him she would keep him informed. She really dreaded calling Determined, so she put off calling for a while longer. Since the new foal would not arrive until late spring, everyone settled into the winter schedule.

Girl took responsibility for Christmas Eve dinner and a scaled-down version of the family traditions. Everyone and everything was arranged to fit into her small apartment. At feeding time on Christmas morning, Missy had special news to share with Sister, who had come by with her family on the way to Brother's home. Girl had accepted an engagement ring the evening before. The wedding date was not set but would likely be in June, after her graduation as a registered nurse. When Sister asked how Missy felt about the news, she told her it felt easy. All the years of watching Girl grow up had had an even smoothness to them. Girl had always planned ahead. Missy's dad used to say of Nana, "She planned her work and worked her plan." Girl not only looked like her grandmother, she thought a lot like Nana did.

After the winter holidays, Old Mama remembered the weather continued with dense and dreary fog. Even with the indoor facilities, the boarders and lesson students came less often. There were colds and flu going around and many cancellations in the routine at the stables. Since the numbers of horses needing exercise and care remained the same, there was more work for Missy. Even though he was busy at college, Boy made time to be at the stables more. Sister, too, rearranged her home schedule with her husband to watch their children so she could spend more time at the stables.

One Saturday, while Missy was away with Girl, Boy and Sister redecorated the lounge. They had made their plans while Boy exercised Old Mama. They packed up the pictures and wallpapered one sidewall with a spring mural. They hung new drapes and barely finished before Missy got home. They were so excited, to them it looked like a brand-new room. Boy said it was nice what a little paper and paint could do. They were anxious for Missy's reaction. Boy brewed some coffee just before his Mom was due to be back. He and Sister sat down and looked at the room and each other. They could not think of another thing they could change. Just then Missy came into the stables. Watching her move, Boy and Sister thought she looked relaxed and happy. She and Girl had been doing some pre-wedding planning. Boy waited and timed his appearance just right. He called to his Mom to come see what they had done. Missy was already almost at the stairs. She only hesitated a second. She came up and sank down in her dad's old leather chair. She drank the coffee Boy served and admired the job they had done. From that time on, the three of them spent a lot of time in the lounge between their chores and responsibilities at the stables.

Old Mama remembered that winter as the time she and Missy enjoyed Boy. Since he was spending so much time at the stables, he even did some of his school work in the lounge.

Every so often, in the conversations between Missy, Boy and Sister, someone would bring up Eager. One day, Sister laughingly said he made her think of the bunny in the battery ad. He just kept going and going and going. He was traveling all over the states and even to foreign countries. Sister said she heard he had gone to South America. Boy thought it was pretty amazing that the seed idea Eager received from Wise One, so long ago, had sprouted and taken root in such far away places. There were fellows out there traveling around, giving lessons, and doing demonstrations, fellows who were kids or young men when Eager first started spreading the seed.

Boy said the thing about the seed was, as it traveled, it could change some, in order to fit the environment where it landed. Sort of a hybrid plant could develop. For himself, he liked the idea of being able to visit with Wise One. A tiny twig, from the original plant, was what he wanted to grow up to be. He was thankful Wise One was still accessible to some, and especially to him.

Missy said she remembered an article about Eager's attitude with horses from a magazine over twenty years ago. In the article, Eager was quoted as saying he hoped "that someday some little 4-H kid would be using the ideas and would never even know where the ideas had come from." It looked like that time had come.

The weather drifted into spring, and for Old Mama the time had come to deliver. She stayed with her past history of being predicable. When she began to wax, Boy, Sister and Missy took care of all the details just as Doctor John expected. Missy wrapped her tail and cleaned Old Mama, as she had in years past. In other times, there was usually only one day left to wait. During all the other times, the foals had arrived at night. Missy figured this time would likely be the same. Sister had made arrangements with her family to have the time to stay at the stables.

With a gentle spring rain falling outside, the trio settled into their evening vigil. Boy was gently brushing Old Mama when he noticed she had patches of sweat and he called Doctor John immediately.

Old Mama thought about that night. Then she thought about the waiting she was doing today. Golden Son's entry into the world had taken longer than that of any of her other offspring. She remembered how tired she had gotten, even with the doctor's help. Once, the doctor had had to assure Missy the foal was "a diver," and everything was okay. Everything *was* okay; that little fellow was standing by Old Mama's side at daylight when Girl came to visit. They were a happy family: Missy, Girl and Boy, and Old Mama and Golden Son.

30

After the foal arrived, Old Mama received even more attention. Everyone at the stables had to peek at the new foal. Old Mama remembered Boy was the only one besides Missy who ever came into the stall. Missy would groom and care for Old Mama, as usual, while Boy was making friends with her foal. Boy had been to visit Wise One just before the foal's arrival. Wise One had given him some ideas to work with while getting acquainted with the new foal.

When Old Mama had her other foals, she and the foal had usually spent the summer in a hillside pasture. Old Mama remembered she and Golden Son did not travel far. Their summer was spent in the pasture near the stables, where she had spent the past summer. That was pretty much all right with Old Mama. She did not feel as young as before. Missy was feeding extra supplements to her and to the foal. Old Mama needed all the extra vitamins and minerals she could get to keep up with that bouncy little fellow.

As soon as the foal had arrived well and healthy, Missy called Determined with the news. While she had him on the phone, she brought up her concern about registering the foal. She said she would be having the colt gelded.

Later that day, as Missy groomed and cared for Old Mama, she shared with her the visit with Determined. Old Mama wondered why humankind was so concerned with bloodlines and registration papers. She was more concerned with what horse got the job done. Golden Son was the only nonregistered foal Old Mama produced. After he was safely delivered,

Missy let the stud owner know she would not be seeking registration papers. From the time of his foaling, Missy had declared he would never have a selling price.

Thinking back, Old Mama realized the foal had only been a few days old when Girl brought Fiancé to the stables. Girl was introducing him to everyone, but they came to Old Mama's stall first. He was tall like Boy. Where Boy was bronze, Fiancé was dark-haired, with very blue eyes. Old Mama liked him right away. There had been some stable gossip about him after the engagement was announced. Everyone knew Girl met him at the hospital. They knew he was trained as a physical therapist. He liked to backpack, mountain climb and kayak. He was really into running the wild rivers. In high school and college he had played basketball and ran track. He water-skied and snow-skied. He played tennis and liked to play golf. There was hardly an activity or sport he had not been interested or involved in. He did not know a thing about horses.

A few days after Fiancé came with Girl, he dropped by the barn unexpectedly. He arrived during the quiet time early in the morning. He came while Boy was at Old Mama's stall getting better acquainted with Golden Son. He waited quiet and respectful of Boy's project, until Boy joined him. Missy, grooming Old Mama, noted his consideration and was pleased. As Missy left to go on with her day's schedule, the two young men were left in close conversation in front of Old Mama's stall.

Fiancé had come to ask Boy to be the best man at the coming wedding. But more importantly, he wanted to become acquainted on a deeper level. He knew how important Boy was in Girl's life; nothing would or should change that. He was hoping, over time, he and Boy could connect along avenues other than husband and brother of Girl.

He told Boy he had been very sure of his feelings for Girl for a long time. He had waited to propose until he was more sure of Girl's feelings. The trauma in her life of Nana's death and her parent's divorce had caused such major emotional stresses, he felt time was needed for her to begin to heal. After they both knew where their relationship was going but before he presented the ring, he had gone golfing with her dad. Fiancé said Man was a little flustered when he asked for Girl's hand in marriage. He had thanked Fiancé for his consideration. He said he would be glad to have him for a son-in-law. He had seemed to want to say more, but he had choked up and gone back to the business of the golf. Fiancé told Boy he could not follow where Man went. It was closed emotional territory. Fiancé said he followed Man in the business of the golf ball.

Boy confided that his time with his dad was usually spent in pretty much the same manner. From the time Man left the home, it had been mostly Boy who made the phone calls and set up the meetings. It had surely created questions and doubts for Boy. He had grown up thinking he knew how his mom and dad valued him. He knew by how they interacted with him. For him, the problem that came after the breakup was that his mom had continued to treat him the way it had always been, but his dad was like a stranger. Then, as he looked back through his childhood, he wondered how much he had perceived as Mom and Dad was really just Mom. Man had worked at his job. He had worked at building around the property. He had even worked at his golf game. Had he ever worked at building relationships? Boy had a sense of loss and confusion.

Fiancé agreed that it could leave a person wondering. There seemed to be a generation or so, after folks left family farms and family businesses, where the men folks seemed to identify themselves differently, focusing more on work and accomplishments, than on family. Why, he even knew a fellow a little older than Man, who had preteen grandchildren. When this fellow called his daughter to visit and ask about the children, he still did not know their names.

Fiancé declared, "In my life experiences I have proof that this is not necessarily a man thing. My Grand Uncle, a wonderful old fellow, married to my mother's aunt was definitely a contradiction to the theory 'man was by nature not meant to nurture.' He was born in the late 1800s and had fought in the First World War, the war to end all wars, only to see his sons go off to World War II.

"What I remember most was the later years when my aunt and uncle retired from the family farm, leaving the business in the hands of a son. They kept very busy in their little home. Winters were spent making and mailing Christmas cards and presents. Summer was the vegetable garden and the abundant flowers. I can't remember when my family did not get a Christmas card from them; it was always the first to arrive. There was always a little note about the weather, some updates about all their kids and grandkids, and a little inquiry about everyone in our family. The year my aunt died in the fall, we thought we might lose touch, but the very first Christmas card to arrive was from my granduncle. There was a little note about the weather, news updates about kids and grandkids and a little inquiry about the members in our family, each by name. My mother read the card aloud. We all cried. Everyone knew my aunt had written each child's name and birth date in her Bible as her way of committing each to her God and her memory. After reading the card, we felt just as sure uncle had written us all into his heart, long ago."

The conversation turned back to the upcoming wedding. Girl and Fiancé were planning a small morning wedding in a mountain chapel with a reception brunch following at a nearby bed and breakfast. They both had an emotional bond with the high mountain country. It was where they went to leave work and worries behind.

Old Mama came back to the present with a start. She thought she heard Boy's pickup. She listened intently. She discovered it was someone visiting one of the boarders. She heard them go down the opposite side of the barn. She let her breath out in a little snort. Her right front foot left the ground and returned in a bit of a stomp. She did that sometimes. Missy almost laughed when she caught her doing that last week. Missy had told Old Mama she was getting crotchety and impatient in her old age. Old Mama felt that was not so. She knew she could be as patient as ever—a little at a time. Dozing and reliving the past made time pass quicker.

She remembered that after Fiancé unexpectedly dropped by, he came more often. Both Missy and Boy looked forward to his visits. There was something about him that reminded them of Nana. He certainly was easy to talk to, especially about things a person usually did not discuss. There aren't many folks a person can share much of anything with, really. Old Mama had been aware of that trait in people for years. She knew folks had to feel safe to share feelings.

The time went fast from the engagement to the wedding. Old Mama remembered Boy was away from the stables more. He was involved in competitions up and down the state. Girl teased him about chasing points. Fiancé had observed that Boy was quite competitive, in a way he could appreciate. Boy set goals for himself and worked hard to improve his personal best.

With Boy gone, Girl had arranged her time to help more around the place. Fiancé came often, as he had projects of his own. Girl and Missy spent time in the lounge, looking at the bridal magazines and making plans. Too soon the wedding was a picture album, passing around the barn, for everyone to "ooh and aah" over.

When Husband and Girl were back from their wedding trip, another party was planned at the stables. This party reminded Old Mama of her days back at Determined's barn. It was to be a reception with an informal character. The place would be decorated; there would be lots of food and fun. Games and events would be played on horseback.

Old Mama thought back to the morning of the party. While Missy was feeding her, Boy came stomping towards them. Old Mama had known the young man since his stroller days, and before that. She recognized he was upset about something. Immediately, he demanded to know what was *going on*, just who was responsible for planning this "dog and pony show." Missy was surprised at his comments but chose to answer factually and matter-of-factly. She told him Girl and her husband had asked to use the facilities for a wedding celebration, a bit of a combination of shindig and shivaree. Husband's roots had run to country in a northern state, where shivarees were a custom in his grandparents' day. Missy realized by Boy's expression he was not satisfied with her answer, but he knew it would be the only information available from her. Missy was the sort of person who would give advice and counsel only when asked. What Boy felt pressed to know, he would need to find out from Husband.

Just as Boy turned to leave, the opportunity to find out presented itself. Husband was coming into the barn and as the "good-mornings" were being exchanged, Missy used the time to flee the scene. She had not the vaguest idea why Boy had such a burr and didn't think she wanted to know.

Boy was up close and direct when he turned to Husband and asked, "Why?" He was so upset that Husband had to change gears quickly to catch the question. He spent several moments on, "Why?"

"Why plan this reception around horses? Is Girl behind it?" Boy wanted to know.

Husband waited a moment to begin his answer. He said, "I began to plan the party right after the engagement was announced. I felt it was something that would be fun for Girl because so many special events in her life had been celebrated in much the same way. Without your sister's knowledge, I've been learning on Old Brown Lesson Horse, when no one was here but Missy. I'm making progress and I think I'll do okay in the boot race."

By Boy's expression, he knew that was not the "Why" he needed to answer. Husband knew Boy was in the stage of his life where he was struggling with definitions. What makes a man is easier to feel if one has some patterns. In Husband's own growing up, he had had a close relationship with his two grandfathers. He had had lots of older male cousins and some uncles, even though his father had died when he was a youngster.

In answering Boy, he would be clarifying his own feelings. Husband took a deep breath and said, "I don't feel it is a big ego challenge; I'm not less of a man because I don't know much about horses. Neither am I more of a man if I know everything there is to know about horses. Some people ride horses and some people fly airplanes. Some do both. I fly a plane, but it's not an M-15."

Husband knew Boy had been born into the horse world. He enjoyed and appreciated horses. There was another side of the horse world that Boy did not enjoy or appreciate. He did not relate to riders who became completely obsessed with the world of horses. He found even more difficult the people who became so smitten with the blue ribbon riders that they raised them up as "Horse Gods."

Husband thought about his own metamorphosis, from knowing nothing about horses to throwing a horse party. Likely, it felt to Boy as though he had gone to the "other side."

In all honestly, probably it was a little like the question of why one climbs a mountain, the answer being, of course, because it was there. He assured Boy he did not aspire to be the "Rembrandt of the Riding Stables." However, he might become the parent of a child who did.

31

Old Mama's travels through the past were interrupted by the appearance of Missy. It was not yet feeding time. Likely, Missy, too, was getting impatient with the wait for Boy's and Golden Son's return. From the time of Golden Son's arrival until now, the four of them had spent lots of time together.

Old Mama had not gone to the hill pasture when Golden Son was a very young foal. Boy had spent a lot of time and attention on Golden Son during that time. After Golden Son was weaned, he had gone to a hillside pasture with other colts and an older Baby-Sitter Mare. When he had returned from that adventure, he had never been very far away from the stables.

Boy had achieved an Associate of Arts from the local community college and had decided to postpone any further education. He had decided to concentrate on the business at the stables. He really felt his mom could use the help. He also wanted to use this time to learn as much as he could from the horse. That was an attitude he had gotten from visiting with Wise One. Wise One lived quite near during this time. It seemed an ideal learning environment.

There had been little change around the stables during the next three years. Sister only helped out occasionally. She had begun working in a doctor's office near the hospital. Girl and Husband came often, as Girl had taken over some of the lessons Sister had been responsible for. Husband was quick to notice and repair the little things that wore out and needed replacing. Boy had become responsible for most of the young horses. There was still plenty for Missy to do, but things were less hurried.

Recently, Good Friend had come for a visit. She had been there several days. Missy had been excited to share family news with her that she was going to be a grandmother. She was confident Girl would make a wonderful mother. She had not a doubt the little person would have a loving father and a doting uncle. Good Friend had laughingly added, "and an involved grandmother, too!"

As they spent time together, Good Friend realized Missy was still working at slaying some personal dragons. When Good Friend was alone with Old Mama, she had voiced her concerns. Old Mama had sighed. More than one family member had told her their troubles in the last thirty years.

The time had seemed to rush by from Golden Son's foaling until he was entered in the big horse event. Old Mama had been excited to be able to watch most of Boy's and Golden Son's time together. Missy usually timed her schedule so she and Old Mama could be somewhere near where Boy and Golden Son were working.

Missy and Old Mama had watched Boy and Golden Son go through many stages as they learned from each other. Sometimes it seemed their connection was like a child's teeter-totter. It would see-saw up and down. Boy would get frustrated. Golden Son would get confused. Other times it would seem Boy would be confused as to how to help Golden Son understand what he wanted. Golden Son would become frustrated when he could not understand what Boy wanted from him.

When the two would get into this situation, Boy would unsaddle and groom and care for Golden Son. He would put him into his stall for another time. He was careful to stop and take a fresh start later in the day, or even on another day. Boy did not want to try so hard that he would damage some of the connections they were building.

old Momma's story

Boy told Missy it was a little like whittling something out of wood. When he was in junior high school, he had taken an art class in woodworking. If he tried too hard or got into a big hurry, his knife might slip and make a big gouge. He could be hours undoing the damage he had done. Sometimes that piece of art would seem okay to everyone but him. In the finished piece, he could still see the damage. He always knew it was less than what he had been working towards.

Over the months, Boy began to *feel* more of what Golden Son was about. Boy began to realize when and where Golden Son needed more help to understand what Boy wanted from him. Sometimes, there was just a split second off in Boy's *timing*. This would be enough to cause the see-saw effect.

Boy and Golden Son had continued to work it out. Sometimes Boy would take his concerns to Wise One. Other times he would get a little help from Missy. Boy and Golden Son were moving closer and closer together. Finally, their work was like the antique scales Missy's father had had on his desk. The scales had been used to measure gold in the assayer's office of a mountain town. Missy had been fascinated when her father demonstrated how the scales were used. She was always intrigued when they would sort-of shiver into perfect *balance*. It had been a thrill for her when Boy and Golden Son's connection reached a wonderful delicate balance, just a few weeks before they left for the competition.

Now, they were on their way home from the competition. Boy had called from a roadside rest phone. He had had a bad connection, but he told Missy they were okay and would be home about sunset. He did not tell her how the final placing had been at the show. Something in his voice gave her the feeling everything was not okay.

Missy had led Old Mama up the barn alley, near the door. She was busy with her brush, as usual. The way they were standing, facing the west entry, they would be the first to see the returning competitors.

Just at sunset, they heard the sounds of Boy's pickup. Then they were coming in the west entry. Golden sunset rays framed the bronze young man and the golden horse. Standing in the doorway, framed in gold, they looked so much like the trophy statues given to winners that Missy's heart skipped a beat as she saw them: a golden statue, shiny and beautiful, life-like and lifeless, with no warmth or connection between them. Instinctively, Missy knew they had won the competition and lost something far more valuable. Missy remembered what Boy had said about his junior high art project. She felt sad for Boy and for Golden Son. When the competition had become more important than their connection, they had become a trophy for the crowd. They had left the stables as horseman and horse, and returned as "Horse Gods."

That evening, when Girl and Husband called, Boy quietly accepted their congratulations. After a few minutes of conversation about who was at the horse show, Boy brought up the subject with Husband of a few days backpacking in the mountains. It was arranged they would leave in mid-week and be gone three days.

Life around the stables turned to being routine. Missy talked it all over with Old Mama. Missy talked; Old Mama listened. Missy felt sad Boy and Golden Son's event had gone as it did. Boy was certainly responsible for the choice he had made. She felt some responsibility rested with the audience and the "GP," as she referred to the general public.

Missy was not surprised when Boy returned from the mountains that he had decided to go back to college the following semester. He thought he would study law.

When Boy had been back from the mountains a few days, he mentioned to Missy he had a video of his work from the show. He asked if she wanted to watch it. That evening, when Girl and Husband were at the stables, everyone went to the lounge. They settled in with pizza and pop to view the tape. All the way through the eliminations, Boy and Golden Son looked as relaxed as if they were at home. The reining pattern, the herd work, and down the fence could have been filmed any afternoon here at the stables. Except for the newer saddle and a little silver on the headstall and Boy's good Stetson, Missy already had a video that looked like that. They were the picture of a pair in complete unison. Boy paused the film after the eliminations. Everyone had a short break for moving around and cleaning up after the pizza.

While the video was on pause, Boy told them he had had a good visit with Eager the first days of the show. Eager had left before the finals. Boy added he was glad he had. No one responded to that remark. While the video was on pause, he passed around some photos of Hoss, standing inside his silver booth. Hoss did not look any different than he had in years. Even though he didn't change, his silver work had done nothing but get better each season. His was a very popular booth. He was taking enough orders to keep him busy all winter. Boy had seen Bitsy and her husband. Considering her injuries, she was doing well.

When Girl left the room, Boy turned the machine from pause to stop. He had always been considerate of his big sister. He was especially anxious about her and the coming baby.

When Girl rejoined the group, the video began again. The camera took in the crowd. It looked like a full house. When Boy and Golden Son entered the arena, there was no mistaking this reining pattern was executed for the crowd. Boy's body language was controlled and his movements concise. They received a good score. The film had several other reining performances—then there was a section of herd work. Boy and Golden Son worked second. Watching closely, Missy could see the tension building in Boy. Although not perfect, the work was good enough for a better than average score. There were several other herd works on the film. Some of these works had scores about like Boy's.

Later, Missy told Old Mama she got goose bumps wait-ing for the film of the fence work. In her memory, she had relived some of her own challenging fence works. It was really quiet in the lounge as the group concentrated on the video. The single cow entered the arena and the challenge began. Boy was intent on the screen. Girl was intent on the screen. Missy's eyes never left the screen. Husband's eyes never left Boy's face. He saw Boy's face tighten and his jaw clench, a tiny muscle on his jaw twitched. He put the video on pause. Then he stopped the film a second, reversed it, and then moved it forward to pause again. He snorted, almost the way Old Mama did, when she was frustrated or impatient. Then he let the film roll on to its conclusion. Everyone in the room got to see the awards presentation, everyone but Boy, who left the room to check on Golden Son.

With the film over, Missy went to check on Old Mama. Girl and Husband left for home.

Missy was still at Old Mama's stall when Boy came. As he approached he asked his mom, "Did you see?" Old Mama had noticed years ago that connected people seem to have disconnected conversations. Missy simply nodded, "Yes." Boy seemed to be talking more to himself, than to Missy, when he continued, "He was doing fine! He could have done it without me!"

Missy did not answer. She let him walk away. Her junior high son, who had tried too hard, had gotten into a hurry and slipped.

Missy told Old Mama she had known from the moment he got home what had happened in the finals. Watching the video had only confirmed what she had already known. Most people watching the film would only see a brilliant fence work. Boy would not have needed to pause, stop, reverse, and ad-vance the film for Missy to have known. When the two of them were in weightless connection, in mind, body and purpose, Boy had doubted. In his doubting of Golden Son, he had become Man the Master. Where he really did not need to even suggest, he had demanded. So, like the wooden art piece in junior high, in the work that seemed beautiful and complete to others, Boy could see the damage he had done. He would always know that it was less than he had been working towards.

In the next few weeks, Boy spent much time with Golden Son. His plan was to have things going as well as possible between them before Golden Son was turned out for an extended stay in a large pasture from late fall through the winter.

32

Each day the sun shone less. The rains came every few days. They brought the season of mud and chill winds. Old Mama spent more time inside her stall. She spent more time lying on the soft shavings. As she lay not asleep or awake, her long ago kept moving behind her eyes. She was with her mama her very first summer. The herd was her world and the world had everything and more. She could feel again the excitement of the foal races. In the pure joy of the run, dodging bushes, leaping creeklets, they seemed to leave the earth in abandonment.

Whenever she sensed Missy coming into the stables, Old Mama was always on her feet to greet her. She would look out over the stall door and make her comfort sounds as Missy approached. Old Mama could remember when Missy had come whistling, back when everything was all right. Each time as Missy approached Old Mama's stall, Old Mama could see the Missy of yesterday coming out from behind the rigid posture and clenched jaw. As Missy began the routine of brushing and rubbing, the ritual seemed to give Missy a desperately needed release. Sometimes, she kept up a running commentary. Sometimes, she was mute. Always, she gave a lot and seemed to get even more than she gave. Old Mama knew Missy needed her. Old Mama longed for Missy to be all right again.

Just before the shortest day, Missy came earlier than usual. Old Mama was almost caught napping. Missy brought an excitement with her, a joy the past could not rob, nor the future dim. Today, her first grandchild was entering the world. Everyone already knew the baby was a boy. Since his was a special delivery, they even knew the date and time. For several months now, Missy had been absorbing "Grandma jokes" with a special glow.

After the baby came, the cold damp weather seemed to get damper and colder than Old Mama could ever remember. Old Mama stood inside her stall. Outside in her run, the world was either rain or dense fog. Old Mama dozed and relived her colt season. Missy came at the same time everyday. She was not so rigid. There was a baby smell about her. Old Mama marked her days by Missy's visits.

One afternoon, as Missy brushed and rubbed and talked with Old Mama, they were both startled by the presence of a quiet man. He had entered the stables from the north end. They had not been aware of him until he was beside them. He was not a stranger to Missy. They had shared the same horse sales, horse shows, and other horse events for several years.

Missy knew his ranch was in the foothills. He had a few good Quarter Horses and his cattle went to the forest in the summer. His place was kept up and convenient for both his stock and himself. He was a good manager and it was good management not to stress his livestock or his help. Some of his neighbors thought he was softhearted. His old retired saddle horses lived in his green pastures in the summer and on good hay in winter. When they died, he and Padre took the backhoe up the hill and made them a resting place under the oak. He even made a marker. He was quiet about it. He was a college man. He could talk to anyone about anything. He could be very quiet about many things. In his youth he had buried two infant sons. Five years ago his wife had died, but he never talked about that.

He and Missy talked about national politics, local events, and the weather. Missy voiced her concerns about Old Mama's health. He told Missy about a new formula he had read about.

This supplement was supposed to be just the thing for a special horse like Old Mama. When someone else came into the stables, he tipped his hat and said, "Good bye."

Ten stormy days later he came again, at the same time of the day. He carried a bag of the new formula for Missy to try with Old Mama. He said it had taken a while for his feed store to find the new formula.

Missy paid him for the formula. Missy did not accept favors. He and Missy talked about the formula, the weather, local events, and national politics. When he left, he said he would check back to see how the formula was working for Old Mama.

Missy fed the special formula to Old Mama exactly as directed. Old Mama cooperated with Missy and ate it as expected. She had always chosen to do whatever Missy wanted. She had been a model patient for vet checks, needle pokes, and paste wormer. She wanted to do what Missy wanted. This time, Missy wanted to turn back time. Old Mama knew she couldn't do that for Missy, or for herself. She could only turn back the years in her mind. As the cold and fog seeped in, she was cold even under the extra blankets Missy brought. Those were the times she dreamed about green grass, spring, and colt racing.

Quiet Man came back once or twice more on his way back home after town appointments. One day he mentioned a small horse pasture he had at his ranch. Since he was raising fewer horses, it wouldn't be used. It would be ideal for a few yearlings and Old Mama to pasture in come spring. There was some hillside, some flat meadow, and a little creek that ran in the spring.

Missy's eyes lit up at the prospect. Then she drew away and became stiff. In her "behind the wall" voice she said, "I'll pay you, of course. I do not accept favors!" Quiet Man responded causally, "Oh, we'll figure out a fair rent." He went on visiting about politics, local events, and the weather. Missy came back from behind the wall and joined the casual conversation. Before Quiet Man left, they had settled the subject of the pasture rent and the how and when the horses would be hauled there.

Old Mama found the pasture to be as wonderful as she had dreamed of all winter. All winter her mind had traveled to her first spring. She had lived again and again those times beside her mama in the Golden Stallion's band. There had been plenty of lush feed and fresh cool water. Those spring days had sunshine and showers and good times with the other foals. As Old Mama grazed about the pasture, she enjoyed watching the yearlings, which shared her space. Sometimes their play was so wild and free-they could be grazing on the hillside among the oaks and suddenly "heads up" they were off and running. They would race off the sidehill and jump the little creeklet. They would stop at the fence corner and whirl about as if to say, "Now, wasn't that grand?" They were grand all right, one was a penny colored sorrel, one a red dun, and one a buckskin. They were especially grand to Old Mama. They were the foals of her foal's foals. All carried her bloodline. She was proud of them, so proud of them. Missy was proud of them, too.

Missy came to the pasture every day in the mid-morning. She would park her pickup in the corner, just inside the field. Old Mama would come to greet her. Missy was still feeding her the special formula every day. Missy was counting on the formula to rejuvenate Old Mama. Often Missy brought her new grandson. She was so proud of him. Old Mama was proud of him, too. He didn't do much yet but sleep in his car seat while Missy fed Old Mama. Quiet Man often joined them. He would just happen by on his way around the ranch. He would stay for a while and visit about the stock market, cattle futures, and the latest horse sales. Then he would drive off in his old blue pickup. He called it the "ranch pickup." He drove a shiny gray pickup for town trips.

Old Momma's Story

Old Mama began to notice a change in Missy. Her touch was different and she moved in a softer way. Old Mama longed for Missy to be all right. How she needed Missy to be all right again. Even with the formula, the green grass, and the longer spring days, Old Mama felt her days growing shorter. She had always given whatever Missy wanted. But this was a different call. From long ago and far ahead, Old Mama felt the pull of the wild bunch. Still, she was there every day by the fence corner to greet Missy and whoever else came along, Quiet Man or Grandboy.

Then a day came like no other. The green grass was so vivid, the sky true blue with just a kindergarten cloud or two. Missy came a little earlier than usual, whistling. Old Mama was finishing her formula when Quiet Man came. He was carrying a catalog from a recent horse sale. He had it all marked with prices and comments. He had stories to tell. He said he had even bought an older mare with her spring foal. Missy and Quiet Man did not even notice when Old Mama moved away. She slowly crossed the little creek, being careful not to slip on the mud-lined bank. She grazed her way up across the meadow where it raised up toward the oaks.

Old Mama looked back at Missy and Quiet Man. They were leaning over the hood on his old pickup looking at the catalog. Grandboy was asleep in his car seat in Missy's truck. Old Mama raised her head and looked again, *really looked*. A rush of joy ran through her veins. Missy is okay. Missy is all right!

Just as this knowledge settled in, Old Mama felt the rush of the colt race. In a flash of color they flew by her. As the copper colt charged by, Old Mama whirled and joined the chase. When they reached the creek, they were airborne to the other side. In one last leap of joy, Old Mama left the ground, stretching toward the other side. As she reached the top of her arch, she saw them on the other side, her mama, the other mares and foals, and the Golden Stallion. In a rush of joy she joined the Wild Bunch. They left together.

When Old Mama's heart stopped in mid-air, her body fell quite awkwardly. The soft mud along the bank cushioned her head. Her tail floated in the flowing creek. The sight and sound of her fall momentarily took the breath from Missy. Then she was beside her. Missy lifted Old Mama's head from the mud and cradled it against her. Her anguish so raw and pain so deep, she was aware of nothing. Over and over she chanted, "Oh, No.....!, Oh, No.....!, Oh, No....!" The Grandboy slept. Quiet Man stood quietly. Then from deep within Missy came another sound. The anguish of a wounded animal. She wound her fingers in Old Mama's mane; her body rocked with each wave of pain— finally, the long overdue tears came.

Quiet Man stood silent, poised between Missy and the sleeping baby. He watched the flood of tears roll back the years. He saw the loss of a woman betrayed wash by, finally the jerky sobs of a child of twelve, exhausted and in need of comfort. He knew he was on sacred ground. Just then he heard the baby begin to wake. He moved quickly to meet Missy's need for comfort, before she needed to be a comforter.

With a strong hand on her shoulder, he spoke her name. She rose and stood against him as he stroked her hair and consoled her as a father would his child. Just then the baby's waking sounds became more demanding.

Missy grew up quickly. She stepped away from him, a grandmother. He had felt the change coming with the baby's first sound. Just before the final change, he spoke, "The baby needs you. If you would like, I'll do you a favor, go get Pedro, and take care of things here."

Missy stiffened. Then as she released the board between her shoulders, she met his eyes. The breath she was holding slipped out as she accepted and said, "Thank you for the favor."

Afterward

Horses are my everyday world. I work around them—on them—I spend most of my time with them. Growing up on a ranch in Tuscarora, Nevada, I have always been acquainted with horses. Much like Determined's family in the first part of this book, I, too, have had my share of barn animals—sheep, leppy calves, goats, and they were all special in their own way—but none of them could compare to the horse.

My family has been raising horses and cattle for four generations now. The cattle are our livelihood and the horses are our partners in maintaining the cattle. Even though the cattle are the livelihood for the ranch, it is the horse that becomes a partner in getting the job done. We raise a lot of horses here on our ranch and we take a lot of pride in making a good solid ranch horse that is gentle, well trained, and versatile. In the company of friends, we also have a production sale each fall in Elko, Nevada. We sell everything from baby colts to finished bridle horses.

We also show our horses in working cowhorse competitions and local cuttings. The Elko County Fair is the epitome of all the county fairs in Nevada. It is one of the few county fairs in the West that I know of that still celebrates by having stock competitions in the old tradition, which takes a horse through the classes from the Snaffle Bit to the Hackamore, then to the Two Rein and finally the Bridle. Along with the stock horse classes, the fair hosts branding contests and team sorting and team roping. The fair is one of our annual social events where the whole rural community gathers: some to compete, some to fellowship, but most to support the traditions of our way of life.

Even though I have been on horseback all my life—ridden hundreds of different horses—there have been only a few really special horses. These are the ones that seem to know what you are thinking before you ask something of them. They are the ones with the personalities that a good horseman recognizes as something special. They are the horses you give a little extra grain to, spend a few more minutes brushing and cleaning up, the one partner you can confide in when you have something on your mind. This horse is special, not because he will listen to you or nicker at you when he sees you, but because he has gained your respect. He is something stable you can depend upon because he is your partner and he will give you one hundred percent and do it with style.

Horses are one of many precious gifts from God, and master horsemen are a blessing to many people; however, the horse can sometimes become so much a part of some people's lives that their whole existence depends upon them. These people are looking for something to fill some void in their lives, and the horse or the idolization of master horsemen begins to fill that void—until instead of being gifts or blessings from God—they become something to worship in themselves. I believe there is only one true God. When we try to replace Him with something He has created, we all lose out.

I enjoy my horses—they are truly a part of me—but they are not first in my life. I try to make my Lord Jesus Christ first—my family second—and everything else third. That way, I worship God instead of His gifts.

—Ty Van Norman, April 2001

About the Author

Born Milly Randall in the small, self-contained community of Bruneau, Idaho, in 1929, Milly Hunt Porter was raised on a family farm where she learned both responsibility and husbandry at an early age, tending the farm animals and doing daily chores. A child during the Great Depression and a teenager during World War II, Porter came to prize the qualities of thrift and ingenuity which she garnered during those periods.

Porter's adult years were spent raising a family of four on Nevada and California cattle and horse ranches. Since, during those years, horses provided both the family livelihood and a major source of recreation and entertainment, horses soon became a major focus in Porter's life.

Porter utilized her knowledge of horses in 1978 when she was the editor of *Think Harmony with Horses* by Ray Hunt and again in 1987 when she edited Tom Dorrance's *True Unity*. Both books explore the relationship between horse and human.

Between editorial projects, Porter published *Hey Elko*, a collection of her original verse, inspired by the city and county of Elko, Nevada.

Porter began work on *The Horse Gods* in 1994, first writing the conclusion to the novel, and then allowing the rest of the story to unfold "in much the same fashion that life weaves its drama—events and characters wandered in and influenced the flow of people's lives."

Porter has now returned to Bruneau, Idaho, where she lives on a farm once again with her present husband George. After fifty years away, the return was a homecoming: "It was as though I had stepped out on my left foot and just stepped back in on my right foot—a comfortable and comforting feeling."